ARMING THE HEAVENS

ARMING
THE
HEAVENS

*The Hidden Military Agenda
for Space, 1945–1995*

JACK MANNO

DODD, MEAD & COMPANY, New York

Published by Dodd, Mead & Company, Inc.
79 Madison Avenue, New York, N.Y. 10016
Distributed in Canada by
McClelland and Stewart Limited, Toronto
Manufactured in the United States of America

FIRST EDITION

Library of Congress Cataloging in Publication Data

Manno, Jack.
    Arming the heavens.

    Bibliography: p. 218
    Includes index.
    1. Astronautics, Military.   2. Space weapons.
3. Space warfare.   I. Title.
UG1520.M36   1984   358'.8   83-20659
ISBN 0-396-08211-4
ISBN 0-396-08212-2 (pbk.)

*For Dianna Marie, whose birth came in the middle
of writing Chapter 5, in the hope that she will
grow up to look to the heavens in awe and wonder
rather than fear and despair*

Contents

Acknowledgments

This book has been a major undertaking and many people have assisted in one way or another. I thank Cindy Squillace for her invaluable contributions; Henry Jankowitz for reading the first draft and giving many long hours to criticism of the ongoing work; William Sunderlin, Joe Bachman, Ron Shuffler, and Dik Cool for assistance in research and formulating many of the ideas in the book; Bob Bowman and Carol Rosin for their time and inspiration; Karen Mihalyi, Jan Phillips, Geoff Navias, Richard Gardner, Kath Buffington, Mary Anne Squillace, Linda Perla, Jeanne McCormick, Dan Gale, Melinda Wheeler, Dory Sokol, Roz Jacobs, Edie Birch, Terri Manno, Eileen Gallagher, Harry Birch, Kevin Osborne, Sylvia Sunderlin, and my mother and father for friendship and kindnesses. I also acknowledge the Syracuse Peace Council, the oldest independent local peace organization in the United States, for the work that they/we do, for the help they have given in shaping my political and moral perspectives, and for the hope they have given me that we *can* change the world.

Introduction

It has long been hoped that humanity, humbled by the immensity of space and the comparative minuteness of the earth, would finally abandon its military and imperial ambitions. Two thousand years ago, the Greek author Lucian wrote about an imaginary trip to the moon. His hero, carried aloft on the left wing of a vulture and the right wing of an eagle, remarked how trivial earth's quarrels seemed when viewed from the heavens.

> The whole of Greece as I saw it might measure some four inches; how much smaller Athens on the same scale. So I realized what sort of sized basis for their pride remains to our rich men. The richest of all, methought, was the proud cultivator of an Epicurean atom. Then I looked at the Peloponnese and my eyes fell on the Cynurrian district, and the thought occurred to me that it is for this little plot, no broader than an Egyptian lentil, that all those Argives and Spartans fell in a single day.[1]

But as civilization progressed and the world grew smaller, Lucian's perspective on conflict was reversed. Warfare's potential seemed increased rather than diminished. Militarists who once would have fought over a district "no broader than an Egyptian lentil" could now see and dream of controlling the entire globe.

No sooner was space flight technically possible than strategists, coveting the power orbiting satellites implied, began to plot the capture and control of regions above the earth. From space, large tracts of the globe are simultaneously in view. Points otherwise separated from each other by the curve of the horizon may both still be within spotting range of an orbiting spacecraft.

The use of this vantage point in space has obvious military significance. Live visual communications can be routed via satellite from a battle in one part of the world to a commander in another. Both the

1

launch sites and targets of intercontinental ballistic missiles can be sighted, and aiming and firing can be accurately guided from space. Increasingly sophisticated reconnaissance devices can monitor every spot on earth. As methods of communication, espionage, navigation, information processing and display become more refined and integrated, they make it possible to transform the earth into an electronic battlefield, its wars observed on display terminals by commanders far from the field.

In 1983, General Bernard Schriever, commander of Air Force programs in space from 1954 to 1966 and author of President-elect Ronald Reagan's transition report on space, explained what he would like to see come about:

> What I want is a radar surveillance system which allows you to spot everything that's moving, either on the surface or above the surface of the earth. And if we had a number of companion systems, a high-energy laser, or particle beam weapon, or something else along with the pointing and tracking ability to knock down airplanes and missiles, then you wouldn't even need to knock out cities; you could knock out forces. You could pin your enemy down on earth. What would they do?[2]

From a position high above the earth, the allure of invulnerability is attractive.

However, while the power potential of that vantage point attracted the military imagination, others like Lucian saw something different. To these members of the first living generation to view the earth from space, their planet seemed small, fragile, and solitary, an oasis in a void otherwise profoundly hostile to life. The image of "the Whole Earth" became an icon; posters and banners appeared with space photos of the planet. The image resurrected in a new form the ancient Earth Mother goddess. Concepts inherent in such slogans as "spaceship Earth," "this island universe," and "planetary consciousness," unheard of before the Space Age, played an important part in stimulating an international movement of environmentalists, antinuclear activists, and pacifists, all of whom urge a unanimous commitment to the care and maintenance of the earth. For them, earth has but one border, the indigo haze that marks where the atmosphere dissipates into space, and any venturing into that region is of international consequence.

But, unfortunately, it is not the vision of good stewardship that has guided the journey into space. Rather, nation states with a baggage of military and imperialist ambitions have taken the lead. It is these ambitions that the space programs have been created to serve. The space-faring nations have made huge investments in space projects, naturally expecting to reap substantial military and economic advantage for themselves.

And yet space is intrinsically an international environment; its most important resource—the broad overview of earth—is obviously global in nature. The tensions arising between the rich space-traveling few and the poor earthbound many over whether space technology is used to promote international cooperation and development or whether the space-faring nations instead expropriate space for strictly nationalist gains, threaten to lead to major conflicts in the twenty-first century. U.S. space policy for the 1980s and 1990s, as it is currently being fashioned, has these conflicts as much in mind as U.S.-Soviet competition in space.

The rise to power of a right-wing president in the United States and the growing confidence among the American military in advanced technology have brought about the latest round in the militarization of space. The accelerated militarization of space in the last part of the twentieth century, with its development of weapons for fighting in and from space, clearly has its roots in the space-war schemes first proposed during the Cold War fifties. At the beginning of the Space Age, anything seemed possible. The Air Force, Army, Navy, and CIA all had space programs under development by the mid-fifties. Faith in technology was absolute. It was widely believed that once the problem of building rockets powerful enough to defeat gravity was solved, succeeding technological hurdles would be vaulted in rapid succession. Those running programs for the military services projected that by the 1980s space flight would be as routine as air flight. Space bombers would be as much a part of the Air Force as fighter jets, and a military base on the moon would be no more remarkable than bases in the South Pacific.

Exploiting space for military purposes, however, turned out to be far more difficult and expensive than the early strategists imagined. Despite

Air Force insistence that space is merely a vertical extension of air space, the day of space-based antiballistic missiles, satellite interceptors, orbiting bombers, air-, sea-, and land-based antisatellite weapons, and all the other schemes concocted in the 1950s was much farther in the future than was originally predicted. Even so, the story of the military space program is the story of amazing technological developments . . . and of political debates, interservice rivalries, and private corporate enrichment—all taking place behind a screen of public deception. Because of the long time intervals between the planning and realization of space projects, the results of strategy debates and political maneuvers in one decade are not seen until the next. The military space program of the 1980s was determined by the decisions made in the 1950s, 1960s, and 1970s; the decisions being made in the 1980s will shape the space program in the twenty-first century.

The decision in the mid-seventies to build the capability to fight and win a prolonged nuclear war changed U.S. space policy. Since satellites on both sides would be directly involved in such a war, the need to defend and destroy satellites was highlighted. They would be indispensable to the command and control of U.S. forces dependent on high-tech weapons systems. *As long as U.S. military policy focuses on the ability and willingness to fight nuclear wars, and as long as U.S. foreign policy assumes America has a claim to the oil in the Middle East and the minerals in Africa and South America—a claim to be backed by threat of force—then the concept of a global battlefield, involving integration of command and control through a network of satellites, will lead inexorably to an arms race in space.*

Space weapons, although they present complex design challenges, are forms of weapons concepts already developed. Every type of land, sea, or air weapons carrier and weapon can be translated to meet the demands of space. The possibilities include space guns, space tanks, space mines, space interceptors, space-WACS (warning and control systems), spacecraft carriers, and space bombers.

With the opening of a space-war arena will come the offense-defense spiral so familiar in the arms race on earth. Every new spacecraft will require internal or external means to defend itself. Once the defensive measure is conceived, it will prompt a new offensive design to counter it. The new offense will contain within it the seeds of a new defense.

Much of this costly leapfrogging will take place even before the new weapon actually goes into production.

And each new stage of the space arms race will find its political and military justification, most likely in reference to Soviet threats, real or imagined. The more the strategists attempt to bring the military situation under their control, the more control will slip away, undercut by some newer weapon, some limit to spacecraft performance dictated by the space environment, some constraints required by a failing economy, until war or chaos brings an end to the arms race and the social institutions that support it.

The real tragedy of an arms race in space will not be so much the weapons that evolve—they can hardly be worse than what we already have—but that by extending and accelerating the arms race into the twenty-first century the chance will have been lost to move toward a secure and peaceful world. Even if militarists succeed in arming the heavens and gaining superiority over potential enemies, by the twenty-first century the technology of terrorism—chemical, bacteriological, genetic, and psychological weapons and portable nuclear bombs—will prolong the anxiety of constant insecurity. Only by eliminating the sources of international tension through cooperation and common development can any kind of national security be achieved in the next century. Space, an intrinsically international environment, could provide the opportunity for the beginnings of such development.

The space program of today has its roots deep in the strategy of world domination through global terror pursued by the Nazis in World War II. Many of the early space-war schemes were dreamt up by scientists working for the German military, scientists who brought their rockets and their ideas to America after the war.

1

The Nazi Legacy

Wernher von Braun was a guru of the cult of space: Engineers followed him from war to war, across national allegiances, from project to project. He oversaw the creation of the V-2 rockets that served as Hitler's Vengeance Weapons, of the U.S. Army's long-range ballistic missiles, and of the NASA Apollo spacecraft that carried astronauts to the moon.

Von Braun's story is legendary. In 1920, at the age of eight, he received a telescope as a gift from his mother, the rich and personable Baroness Emmy von Quistorp, herself an accomplished astronomer. Young Wernher was spellbound by the moon and stars and challenged by how near they seemed. Then and there, the story goes, he dedicated his life to the accomplishment of space flight. At the age of thirteen he set himself the task of inventing a spacecraft to carry him to the moon. Inspired by Hermann Oberth's book *The Rocket for Interplanetary Space*, but unable to comprehend its complicated mathematics, the young astronomer went to see the author in search of counsel about his education. Oberth encouraged him to pursue his scientific studies, which led to degrees in both mathematics and physics from the Charlottenburg Institute of Technology.

When he was sixteen, Von Braun joined the German Society for Space Travel. The group, which had formed in Berlin to investigate Oberth's speculations, began experimenting with crude rockets in an abandoned munitions dump outside the city in 1928. Soon Von Braun and the Society for Space Travel attracted the attention of Major General Walter Dornberger, a branch chief of the German Board of Ordnance. Dornberger had heard rumors about a group of eccentric but talented scientists and engineers who bragged they would soon be able to send a man to an altitude of several miles and would one day be able to travel to Mars in the rockets they were testing on otherwise quiet Sundays in a Berlin suburb. Dornberger became a frequent visitor to the society's launch site and one day made an offer. If the society would make its rockets available to the German army, the society would receive financial support from the government and a real proving ground, as well.

In writing about rocketry, Oberth did not overlook the political and military significance of his work. He predicted that rockets would one day carry bombs at lightning speeds across previously unimaginable distances. Furthermore, there was a profit to be made in manufacturing rocket-launched missiles. But rockets were only part of what he envisioned. The most flamboyant item in Oberth's spacewar armory was a giant orbiting mirror—a disc sixteen hundred miles in diameter consisting of ten individual mirrors, each measuring sixteen miles across, which would focus the sun's rays into powerful destructive beams to set an enemy's cities and croplands afire from space, destroy enemy armies, or even melt polar icecaps, raising the level of the oceans in an imaginative bit of environmental warfare.

The German military had a political and much less futuristic interest in rocketry. The Versailles Treaty ending World War I had placed limits on the kinds of activities the German military could pursue. Germany was forbidden to build offensive artillery. But the treaty said nothing about rockets, a loophole through which Germany might one day rearm without violating the terms of the treaty.

Of the members of the Society for Space Travel, General Dornberger was most impressed by the charismatic Von Braun, who at the age of twenty was already leader of the group. Dornberger successfully recruited Von Braun and put him in charge of rocket development for the Army, and most of the other members of the society soon followed.

In 1933 Adolf Hitler and the Nazi party came to power and quickly began the remilitarization of the German state. The German army created a new division of modern rocket weapons, and Dornberger was put in charge. The German Society for Space Travel—which had until this point maintained open scientific ties with counterparts in the United States, Great Britain, France, and Russia—was ordered to maintain secrecy. The mere mention of the word *rocket* was now considered a breach of military security.

Young Von Braun rose rapidly in the new fascist order. He was a prototypical Aryan, with shiny blue eyes, light blond hair, a brilliant mind, and a dynamic personality, the sort of "superman" who was to inherit the world of the Third Reich.

The German army established Von Braun at the Peenemunde rocket production and testing center, where he proceeded to develop large rockets for a German ballistic missile. (A ballistic missile is a rocket-launched missile that is guided during ascent and freely falling during descent to target.) At the same time the Germans were also developing cruise missiles, or buzz bombs—propeller-driven guided missiles.

On March 27, 1939, Hitler came to Peenemunde for a personal tour and demonstration of the rockets under development. Von Braun and Dornberger showed the Führer around, impressing him with the details of their rockets' capabilities, which, they informed him, could carry a missile from Peenemunde to London. The missile would reach London in five minutes, leaving no time for those at the target end to prepare for the blast. Hitler was impressed enough to order that missile development be financed but, expressing supreme confidence in his air force to do any bombing job sufficiently, fell short of a total commitment to rocket-launched missiles.

In October 1942, Peenemunde's A-5 ballistic missile was successfully fired at a test target 150 miles away. The war in Europe was escalating on all fronts. Hitler decided on a strategy of organized terror from the sky and turned to the new pilotless aircraft his scientists had developed. The buzz bombs and ballistic missiles, which he renamed Vegeltunswaffe (vengeance weapons) 1 and 2 were to be aimed at his enemies' most populous cities. Forty thousand forced laborers from concentration camps and POW camps were put to work building the rockets, missiles, and launch pads.

The successful testing of the V-2 and Hitler's decision to give top priority to the V weapons endowed the missile scientists with a new respectability and sense of importance. Walter Dornberger was promoted to the highest rank, commissioner of the Third Reich. Experimental work based on the theories of Oberth and the Society for Space Travel was begun on a number of rocket-launched weapons. Dornberger approached Hitler with the idea of an aerospace glide bomber for a quick surprise attack against New York, the largest city of Germany's newest enemy, the United States. The space glider would skip along the upper fringes of the atmosphere, reenter to drop its load of bombs, and glide to a landing in the Pacific, where the crew would be picked up by submarine. Even Oberth's orbiting solar mirror was under study, and also a system of orbiting bombardment satellites capable of carrying the atomic bombs Germany was trying to build.

Although no space gliders or bombardment satellites made it off the drawing board in time to be used in World War II, the V-2 made its mark in the last months of the war on the cities of London and Antwerp. It proved to be, until the atomic bombs that landed on Hiroshima and Nagasaki, the world's most frightening weapon. From October 1944 until March 1945, a thousand V-2s landed on the streets of London; another fifteen hundred struck the Belgian port city of Antwerp. The V-2s hurled their missiles faster than sound, a new experience for the war-weary Londoners. The explosion happened first. There was no warning to prompt a run for cover. Only after a confusing moment of silence was the sound of the rocket in flight heard. The V-2, the first mature offspring of the alliance between rocket technology and the will to destruction, left nine thousand Londoners dead.

But the war was drawing to an end, and the V-2s could no longer influence the outcome. On April 30, 1945, Hitler died in his bunker. There would be no more vengeance weapons fired in the war. The rocket works at Peenemunde had been destroyed by Allied bombing, and the rocket scientists there decided to surrender en masse to the Americans.

The legacy of World War II—rockets and atom bombs—established a new level of importance for military technology. Wars of the future, it was widely believed, would henceforth be won by the power of advanced military technology. Superiority could only be maintained by ever greater refinements in weapons development. Accordingly, the scientists who had created the V-2 and the other German advances in guidance and communications technologies were considered the most valuable booty of the war. Representatives of the U.S. Army, Army Air Corps, and Navy, along with representatives of the major military contractors, came to Germany to enlist these scientists in their particular service or corporation.

Although Peenemunde and other German rocket factories were captured and appropriated by the Soviet army, most of the leading rocket scientists, prompted by the fear that the Russians would arrest them as war criminals, had already fled toward the advancing Americans. It wasn't until nearly two years later that the Russians reversed their stated policy and took thousands of German engineers and technicians to the Soviet Union and put them to work under Soviet supervision improving Russia's captured V-2 rockets. The elite of the rocket scientists had already been captured and recruited by the Americans.

Like a professional sports draft, the armed services competed with each other for the right to bring the Germans home. The U.S. Army was by far the most successful. Roger Toftoy, the head of technical intelligence for the Army in Europe, had been studying the V-2s from scraps and duds that landed in England. He was eager to recruit the men responsible. After the Peenemunde survivors surrendered to the American forces, they were turned over for interrogation to Richard Porter, who was in Germany representing the General Electric Corporation, which held the Army contract for the first long-range ballistic missile under development in the United States. Von Braun; his deputy, Eberhardt Rees; and 125 Peenemunde engineers, technicians, and managers were acquired by the Army.

The Air Corps was represented by Don Putt, who had done the design work that made the B-27 bomber capable of dropping the huge Hiroshima and Nagasaki bombs. Among those who later went to work for the Air Force was General Dornberger, who came to the Air Force as a consultant after a brief internment as a war criminal in Great Britain.

The Navy sent Bob Freitag to Germany. He recruited the famed V-1 test pilot Willy Fiedler, who later was responsible for developing underwater launch techniques for the Polaris submarines for which Freitag was chief of planning, and Wolfgang Noggerath, a specialist in jet-engine research for the German air force who later ran Lockheed Corporation's Polaris missile plant.

Between the armed services and the private corporations, the United States eventually adopted nearly one thousand German military scientists, many of whom later rose to positions of power in the U.S. military, NASA, and the aerospace industry.[1]

Von Braun and his V-2 colleagues arrived in Boston on September 20, 1945. There they received cover stories and false identification, then boarded trains to take them to New Mexico incognito in order to avoid arousing the anger of resentful Americans. At White Sands missile base, they began working on rockets for the U.S. Army. They soon launched the world's first two-stage rocket, using a salvaged V-2 as the first stage and a smaller booster rocket that fired when the first rocket burned out. In 1948 they undertook the first experiments in launching primates to the upper edges of the atmosphere aboard a two-stage rocket. In 1949, with the beginning of the Korean War, the Army ordered Von Braun and his rocket team to the Army arsenal at Huntsville, Alabama. They were given the task of producing an intermediate-range ballistic missile to carry battlefield atomic weapons up to two hundred miles. The Germans produced a modified V-2 renamed the Redstone, the Army's first operational ballistic missile. Although the Redstone never carried its assigned payload in the battlefields of Korea, it was successfully tested and became the first working rocket in America's postwar arsenal.

Soon after his success with the Redstone, Von Braun began to emerge as the most dynamic spokesman for America's budding space program. While still living in the barracks at White Sands, he had written a fanciful science fiction account of a voyage to Mars, complete with little green Martians. The book was published and gained a modest audience. He first reached a mass audience with a piece for *Colliers* when that popular weekly magazine ran a series of articles about outer space and the prospects for space flight. The series was extremely popular and the articles were collected into a best-selling book, *Across the Space Frontier*. It was the first time that the notion of space flight was presented as more than a comic-strip fantasy.

Von Braun's article was the clearest, simplest, and most believable account of the mechanics of earth orbit and interplanetary travel yet published for popular consumption in America. The centerpiece of his space strategy was a permanently occupied space station in orbit a thousand miles above the earth, serviced regularly by a space shuttle with supplies from earth. According to Von Braun, the space station would serve as a platform both for astronomers to study the stars without suffering the distorting flicker caused by the earth's atmosphere, and as an observation point from which to watch over the earth. His prose gave the impression that the astronauts aboard the space station would be nothing less than guardians watching over the planet, assuring earthlings that nothing would go awry. "Technicians in this space station, using specially designed, powerful telescopes attached to large optical screens, radarscopes, and cameras, will keep constant watch over every ocean, continent, country and city. Even small towns will be clearly visible. Nothing will go unobserved. Within each two-hour period 1/12 of the globe's territory will pass into view of the space station occupants; within each 24-hour period, the entire surface of the earth will have been visible." [2]

Von Braun was an old hand at exaggerating the military potential of his ideas in order to tap the abundant reservoir of military largesse. In a speech before the American Rocket Society, he urged that immediate attention be given to developing his space station idea into workable plans for an impregnable space fortress. "Improvements of existing weapons, nuclear bombs, high speed bombers and conventional arms cannot keep the U.S. so strong the East will not dare to take the offensive. We need a new concept such as the space station."[3] He predicted that the nation that succeeded in establishing the first space fortress would be able effectively to prevent the establishment of a second by any competing nation. He took a slide show depicting his space station and shuttle combination to the Armed Forces Staff College in 1952 to describe how a space station could be used to launch atomic missiles toward the earth. It would be a perfect attack platform, because it could be defended from retaliation. Using antiballistic missiles from space, a station could both defend itself and thwart counterattack on ground territory by knocking enemy missiles out of the sky.

Von Braun was not alone among former members of the German military to take a strong public role in pushing America's military thinking toward space. Shortly after he came to the United States in 1947 as a consultant to the U.S. Air Force and adviser to the Department of Defense, Walter Dornberger wrote a planning paper for his new employers. He projected a system of hundreds of nuclear-armed satellites all orbiting at different altitudes and angles, each capable of reentering the atmosphere on command from earth to proceed to its target. The Air Force began early work on Dornberger's idea under the acronym NABS (Nuclear Armed Bombardment Satellites). As a variation on NABS, Dornberger also proposed an antiballistic-missile system in space in the form of hundreds of satellites, each armed with many small missiles. The missiles would be equipped with infrared homing devices and could be launched automatically from orbit. This concept was also taken under study by the Air Force in the 1950s. Labeled BAMBI (Ballistic Missile Boost Intercept), it was an idea that would reappear in the space-war dreams of the Reagan administration in 1983.

Dornberger's pet project was the aerospace glide bomber he had proposed to Hitler. In 1950 he was able to interest Bell Aviation Corporation in taking on early development work on the glide bomber. Dornberger became a Bell vice-president and recruited another former German army scientist, Krafft Ehricke, to join him at Bell. Ehricke had been an adviser on the German wartime atom bomb project. The Air Force subsequently contracted with Bell to work on Dornberger's space bomber.

Before a congressional hearing in 1958, Dornberger insisted that America's top space priority ought to be to "conquer, occupy, keep, and utilize space between the earth and the moon." In an address to a National Missile Industry Conference, he dismissed NASA's early space-flight program as "space stunts" and urged that more attention be given to space weaponry. "Gentlemen," he told the missile men, "I didn't come to this country to lose the Third World War—I lost two."[4]

That Americans could listen to such advice on how to prepare for World War III in space from their former enemies so soon after World War II is testimony to how quickly and thoroughly the Soviet Union had been transformed from an antifascist ally to America's major enemy. Planning and arming for World War III began even before the Japanese surrendered. The way both the Soviet Union and the United States took their first steps into the Space Age had everything to do with how each perceived the other in relation to the next war.

2

ICBMs, Satellites, and Politics

The work of Walter Dornberger and Wernher von Braun set an ambitious agenda for fielding a military space force of the future: a manned space station as a command and reconnaissance post, an earth-to-space shuttle for logistics, space-to-earth bombardment satellites, maneuverable aerospace planes capable of performing both as spacecraft and as conventional aircraft, a space-based antiballistic missile system, and a variety of antisatellite weapons. By the mid-1950s this space armada had been thoroughly conceptualized and described; its eventual realization became and remained the ultimate goal of the most extreme space hawks throughout the following decades to the present time. In general, those who lobbied for the creation of a U.S. space force ignored economic and political factors in favor of technological futurism and believed that space power would result from the simple extension of the technologies and strategies of air power vertically into space. In contrast to these military futurists, another, more realistic pattern of military space thinking emerged at the same time, immediately following the Second World War. Rather than imagining outer space as a new arena of combat, these strategists, mostly scientists connected with Air Force Project RAND, saw the potential for exploiting orbiting spacecraft in support of conventional military activities on the ground, in the air, and at sea.

Project RAND was a creation of the commander of the U.S. Army Air Corps, General "Hap" Arnold, who had grown concerned over the number of scientists leaving the Air Corps after the war to return to their former employers, the universities and civilian industries. Arnold believed that future military superiority depended on new advances in technology. He sought some means to slow what he saw to be a dangerous brain drain. Arnold proposed the formation of a center where the best scientific and technical minds could be kept busy in research on advanced weapons development. Air Corps Project RAND (an acronym for research and development) was established, eventually to become

the RAND Corporation, initially a division of the Douglas Aircraft
Company under contract to the Air Corps. RAND's first assignment
was to determine the feasibility of earth-orbiting satellites. The resulting
report, written in 1946 and entitled "A Preliminary Design for Experimental World Circling Spaceships," pointed out how such spaceships
might be ideal for improving long distance over-the-horizon communications, which then depended on radio wave reflections off the fickle
ionosphere; for improving ocean navigation with a system based on
receiving a signal from a satellite in a fixed orbit; and for obtaining
critical intelligence information, including mapping potential enemy
targets by means of spaceborne sensors. According to the RAND scientists, artificial satellites for improved communications, navigation, and
reconnaissance would be feasible, given steady progress in the fields of
rocketry and electronics. Unlike the piloted spacecraft and orbiting
bombers envisioned by the Germans, RAND's "world-circling spaceships" would not require unforeseen, dramatic, technological breakthroughs.

A split was apparently developing between the space hawks, who
hoped to extend military action and U.S. superiority high above the
planet, and more sedate strategists, who viewed the more extravagant
spacewar concepts as naive and irrelevant to foreseeable military situations. Perhaps more than any other factor save the constraints of physics
and money, this split, and the compromises reached between its poles,
determined the future course of development of the U.S. space program, both military and civilian.

Out of the RAND work grew the early Air Force development projects on instrumented, pilotless spacecraft for communications, navigation, early warning, and reconnaissance. At the same time, speculative
and some developmental work began on manned spacecraft, aerospace
gliders, satellite interceptors, as well as bombardment satellites and
moon-based weapons. These early study projects, decidedly futuristic,
were among an almost unlimited array of weapons systems conceived as
the result of World War II's technological developments. These systems
included nuclear, chemical, biological, psychological, and environmental weapons; new designs for ships, planes, tanks, and submarines;
guided missiles launched from the air, the ground, the ocean surface,
and under the sea; new forms and methods of propulsion; new methods
for sensing and observing movement on the ground, under water, and

in the air; new means of communication and encryption; and orbiting spaceships and intercontinental missiles. Each weapon and design concept had its own compelling justifications for development and an interest group to argue for it.

In order to have funded all the postwar concepts, the nation would have been required to sustain a level of military spending at least as great as during the war. For the American people, however, the end of the war had meant a time to rejoice and an end to the economic hardships the fighting had demanded. Americans were impatient with the Truman administration for its slowness in filling the shelves with the consumer goods absent from the stores during the war. It would have been politically untenable for Truman to raise taxes and ignore the needs of the domestic economy in order to fund all the projects being suggested by the various military services. It would have been equally difficult to justify continued high levels of military spending when the United States had emerged from the war clearly the world's leading military power. America's monopoly on atomic weapons presented a formidable threat to any of its potential enemies. In addition, Truman believed that national security depended as much, or more, on a sound economy as on a powerful military, and therefore placed strict budget ceilings on all areas of military spending with an overall limit on the military budget of $15 billion. Given Truman's budget ceilings, there was little chance of funding military space projects at anything more than the study project level.

In order to bring some coherence to the many areas of research being opened up, the Truman administration undertook to establish priorities for military research and development. Top priority went to those areas with demonstrated potential in possible near-term conflict situations. Besides improving and testing atomic weapons, guided missiles were among the top priorities—not ICBMs, however, but air-to-air and air-to-surface missiles for the Air Force's bombers, and short-range missiles for ground combat. Although development work continued on long-range ballistic missiles, the programs were not funded at a significant level. Satellite development programs were also continued within the Air Force, but with minimal support from the administration.

Although the president and his economic advisers may have been determined to keep a lid on spending and to balance the federal budget, the events that occurred in the late 1940s, initiating the Soviet-American Cold War, created powerful political pressures to increase all areas of military spending on research and development.

World War II left global turmoil in its wake, aborting the already tentative East-West antifascist alliance and returning Soviet-American relations to their prewar state of mutual distrust and hostility. Soviet Premier Josef Stalin was predisposed by ideology and past experience of Western intervention to view America's atomic bombs and long-range bombers as a serious and credible threat. In addition to Soviet expansionism, Stalin's purpose in stationing large ground forces in Eastern Europe was not only to create a buffer against future ground attacks from the West but to threaten an invasion of Western Europe as a deterrence to an American A-bomb attack. At the same time, Stalin concentrated limited Soviet technological and productive capacity on developing a Soviet A-bomb, and the means, including large rockets, to carry them over intercontinental distances.

American leaders were equally predisposed, from two decades of antibolshevism before the war, to view Soviet actions in Eastern Europe as a direct political and military threat to the West. In 1947, President Truman explained his policy to contain Communist expansion. Prior to the outbreak in 1950 of the war in Korea, Truman maintained that U.S. policy should emphasize the political stabilization and economic renewal of Western Europe. American military strategy would rely on the atomic threat, thereby avoiding a major, and expensive, military presence surrounding the Soviet Union. This policy, which became known as the Truman Doctrine, also served as the rationale for U.S. aid to the government of Greece, then embroiled in a Communist-led civil revolt, and the government of Turkey, a German ally in the war. It was in Germany, and Berlin in particular, where the two sides faced each other and jockeyed for a settlement each perceived to be in its national interest. U.S. policy emphasized the economic revival of the German economy. The Soviets, however, hoped to see a weakened, neutral Germany drained of resources and incapable of rearming and striking eastward as it had done twice in thirty years. The Americans hoped to see a revived Germany as a strong trading partner and a barrier to the westward spread of Soviet influence. The contradictory goals for the future of Germany and the status of Berlin led to the most dangerous confrontations of the early Cold War. By the 1950s the issues were far from settled.

In the fall of 1949, the Soviet Union successfully exploded an atomic device. The day when the Soviets could threaten the United States with atomic devastation was approaching. Within weeks of Soviet A-bomb success, Mao Tse-tung announced the establishment of the Communist People's Republic of China. Despite the long history of Mao's independence of action, Americans tended to perceive the Chinese Communists' victory as yet another step on the path of Soviet expansionism. The signing of a Sino-Soviet treaty of cooperation seemed to confirm this view.

On January 31, 1950, the president directed the Departments of State and Defense to join in a review of overall U.S. policy objectives in light of the changing world situation. The result was National Security Council Document 68, known as NSC-68. It set the tone and substance of subsequent U.S. policy in the Cold War in response to what the document's author described as the "Kremlin's design for world domination." Since the United States was the Soviet's foremost "competing system of power," the Kremlin would be driven by its own ideology to do whatever it could to undermine and weaken American power, the document concluded. It urged that a "bold and massive program" of rebuilding U.S. and Western European military power be undertaken with the goal of attaining clear superiority over the Soviet bloc. And it challenged Truman's budget limitations, arguing that America was rich enough to afford spending up to 20 percent of its Gross National Product on its military, or $50 billion at the time. NSC-68 was a call to arms in a holy war against intransigent evil. It spared no means short of World War III to thwart the Communist enemy. It proposed to strengthen internal security measures; launch a domestic propaganda campaign to stir the populace and elicit the requisite sacrifice and discipline; and initiate covert operations, including terrorism and economic sabotage within the USSR.[1]

While this document was being prepared, the army of North Korea invaded southward, offering yet further evidence of Communist expansionism. Although Korea may have been an unlikely peninsula for the West to attempt to halt what it was coming to perceive as a design for world domination, the confluence of events and fears of the late 1940s brought the U.S. into a war. Without the North Korean invasion, Truman may have been reluctant to accept the budgetary recommendations of NSC-68, but with a hot war with the Communists at hand,

and the emergence of McCarthyism as a political force at home, the administration increased the Defense Department budget from $13.5 billion for Fiscal Year 1950 to $48.2 billion in FY 1951. The basic premise of NSC-68—that only a massive, worldwide American military machine could respond to the Soviet challenge—became an accepted fact of postwar life for America's leaders. In response to the North Korean invasion, the U.S. established a ring of air bases surrounding the Soviet Union with nearly two thousand bombers capable of striking within its borders.

NSC-68 accelerated America's progress toward becoming a military power with farflung commitments. It would only be a matter of time before technological developments turned strategic thinkers toward an understanding of the value of earth-orbiting satellites and their potential to facilitate planet-spanning communications and intelligence gathering for a military machine spread out around the globe.

The same year the Korean War broke out, 1950, RAND Corporation scientists studying the feasibility of long-range ballistic missiles concluded that due to their potential for high-speed surprise and their invulnerability in the foreseeable future to a Soviet preemptive first strike, that ICBMs would be of great military value. The U.S. Army was gradually improving upon its captured V-2s with a rocket now known as the Redstone, after the Redstone Arsenal in Huntsville, Alabama, where Von Braun and his V-2 colleagues were at work on an intermediate-range rocket for missiles to be used in Korea. Concerned about the Army's early lead in rocket development and the possibility that "robot missiles," as guided missiles were sometimes called, might one day replace bombers as the preeminent carrier of the nation's atomic threat, the Air Force moved to consolidate its missile work under a new Air Research and Development Command. Meanwhile, a young senator from Texas, Lyndon Johnson, openly criticized the Truman administration for its slowness in funding the Air Force missile program. Missile development, and its accompanying interservice rivalry, had entered the public domain as a hot political issue. And Lyndon Johnson was already attaching his rising star to an issue he would exploit for the next decade.

Although Truman's 1951 and 1952 military budgets contained across-the-board increases in all areas, there was still not enough money for crash programs in the development of exotic technologies. The administration placed priority in four areas: first, the production of battlefield-size atomic weapons to beef up America's promise to meet Soviet advances anywhere they might occur along the perimeter established by the Truman Doctrine; second, the creation of numerous new air bases both at home and overseas; third, the establishment of four new Army units to serve in Western Europe; and fourth, the rearmament of West Germany within the NATO alliance.

ICBMs would no doubt be devastating weapons. But in the early 1950s the most advanced rockets available could lift only light loads and carry them only relatively short distances—and inconsistently at that. Furthermore, the long-distance guidance systems required to make ICBMs acceptably accurate were well beyond the available technology. An American ICBM may have been conceivable, but only as a generous extrapolation from what was available. Operational missiles would have required significant technological advances in all the interrelated areas of rocket fuels, fuel handling and storage, ignition systems, materials processing, rocket staging, nose-cone design, guidance systems, and warhead design—all of which would have meant a huge government investment of time and money. Given America's apparent superiority in air and naval power, and the Soviet's comparatively primitive technological base, it was an investment the Truman administration determined to be premature and unnecessary. Still, each of the services continued vigorous, if underfunded, research and development programs in all areas of rocket and missile technology. The situation in the Soviet Union was considerably different.

Scientific speculations about interplanetary travel, as well as experimental rocket research, had been extensively carried out in the Soviet Union since the 1920s; the preliminary knowledge with which to begin a missile and space program was already in hand. Soviet leaders, no doubt seeing intercontinental missiles as a potential short cut to global military power and a balance to America's air and naval superiority, concentrated their country's limited technological capacity on the development of powerful rockets for ICBMs. Sometime in the early 1950s, the Soviets also adopted a strategy for a national space program. By 1954, while American space efforts were scattered among competing services with conflicting goals, the Soviets had established a permanent Committee on Interplanetary Communications to "coordinate and direct all work concerned with the problem of mastering cosmic space." [2]

The Soviets chose to focus on the interrelated tasks of long-range missilry and space flight. Eventually, all their early space shots were launched by an ICBM booster, the culmination of a decade of Soviet rocketry.

The difference in organization, capacity, and priorities between the early Soviet and American missile and space programs established the difference in character of each nation's space program as it developed in the succeeding years. The United States simultaneously pursued a variety of missile and military satellite projects, its superior resources under comparatively looser control spread out among various interests. The Soviets single-mindedly organized themselves to produce large booster rockets. Even at this early stage both nations were entering the space age with one eye turned toward the stars, while the other kept watch for military advantage on earth. The tremendously costly missile and space race that eventually distorted the economic and political development of both nations and crippled the prospects for international cooperation in space exploration could only have been avoided by concerted efforts to reduce both sides' reasons for fear and distrust.

In 1952 the International Congress on Astronautics voted to ban its members from using astronautical research for military purposes. The International Congress urged that space stations, once established, be open to visitors from all nations and expressed hope that space exploration could be organized on an international basis. It was the first such call for international cooperation in space.

With the Truman administration tied up with the war in Korea and the growing tensions of the Cold War, little effort was made to deal with the issues of missiles and space—neither how America's efforts would be organized, nor toward what ends. The decisions that would determine the future of U.S. activity in space were left to the new administration of Dwight Eisenhower, inaugurated in January 1953.

Groomed and promoted for the presidency by a coalition of elite American business interests, Eisenhower entered the White House with a typical Republican agenda. He promised to cut taxes and deficit spending and to ensure sustained economic growth. Despite a Republican platform that had promised the military more firepower and a commitment to containment, Eisenhower, with the urging of Treasury Secretary George Humphrey, was looking for ways to cut the Defense

budget he had inherited by one-third. Military spending had qua-
drupled between 1950 and 1953.

Eisenhower had been critical of Truman's failure to articulate a
strategy to back his policy of containing the Soviet threat. Despite
Truman's ever-increasing military expenditures, the United States was
involved in a bloody, stalemated war in Korea, which was devastating
the nation it was ostensibly being waged to protect.

In 1953 the Eisenhower administration initiated what it called a
"New Look" at American military strength. According to the new strategy that resulted, the United States would place primary emphasis on
nuclear weapons and thereby maintain its military power while reducing conventional force levels and military expenditures. The new policy
came to be known as the policy of "massive retaliation." Secretary of
State Dulles defined it as "the will and . . . the means to retaliate
instantly against open aggression by Red Armies so that, if it occurred
anywhere, we could and would strike back where it hurts, by means of
our own choosing." [3] Rather than promising to clash with the Soviets
anywhere along the boundary defined by the Truman Doctrine,
Eisenhower threatened to unleash America's nuclear power as retaliation against Soviet transgressions. Matching military might with strategy, Eisenhower placed top priority on the Strategic Air Command's
long-range bombers, accelerated the testing and stockpiling of nuclear
weapons, and gradually cut the size of the Army. In May 1953
Eisenhower issued a veiled threat to bring atomic weapons onto the
Korean battlefield. This threat, along with other circumstances, including the death of Stalin and the Soviet new rulers' apparent willingness to
sponsor negotiations, led to an armistice.

The policy of massive retaliation threatened to lower the threshold at
which nuclear weapons would be used. The Soviet's extreme vulnerability to the very powerful strategic nuclear bomber force, and
Washington's stated willingness to use nuclear force, became an incen-
tive to the Soviet military to attain, as rapidly as possible, an intercontinental bombardment capability with which to deter America from
considering a nuclear first strike.

Eisenhower's foreign policy toward the rest of the world was most
clearly stated in a letter he wrote before his campaign to Earl Schaefer,
the president of the Boeing Aircraft Company. "From my viewpoint,

foreign policy is or should be based primarily on one consideration. That consideration is the need for the United States to obtain raw materials to sustain its economy, and when possible, to preserve foreign markets for our surpluses. Out of this need grows the necessity for making certain that those areas of the world in which essential raw materials are produced are not only accessible to us, but their populations are willing to trade with us on a friendly basis."[4] In order to ensure the "friendliness" of populations and governments, Eisenhower followed a strategy of covert destabilization and, if that failed to attain the desired results, direct military intervention to topple governments he perceived as hostile to U.S. trade interests. This happened most notably in Iran and Guatemala.

The coming missile and Space Age could only disrupt Eisenhower's policies. The maintenance of clear U.S. military superiority was essential to making the threat of nuclear retaliation believable and to maintaining a free hand for U.S. intervention in the Third World. The United States had unquestioned superiority in bombers, bombs, ships, and submarines. Long-range missiles and space platforms armed with nuclear weapons would disrupt the existent military equation. Eisenhower preferred to focus on and improve America's clear advantages rather than open another unpredictable area of the arms race. A major effort in rockets, long-range missiles, and satellites might not only undermine his military policy, but also destroy his economic program by unleashing a flood of demands on the nation's treasury.

Eisenhower, however, was unprepared to deal effectively with the apparently uncontrollable momentum of the new technology. This was spurred on by interservice and intercorporate rivalries and supported by a powerful new coalition of interests that included young Air Force officers enamored of the new technology, aerospace entrepreneurs, politicians currying favor with the new industries, and anti-Communist fanatics eager to wage the ultimate battle with the Reds and be done with it. Rockets, missiles, and spacecraft were quickly becoming the prestige items of an alluring new military field. The grave moral, social, and political implications of a Soviet-American missile and space race were ignored by those intent on getting in on this exciting new area of enterprise from the start.

In the Air Force, the dynamic and brash general in charge of space and missile programs, Bernard Schriever, was winning notoriety and respect in aerospace circles for demanding that greater attention and resources be given rockets and missiles. This was against the wishes of the powerful head of the Strategic Air Command, Curtis LeMay, who looked upon the development of ICBMs as a threat to the strategic preeminence his beloved B-bombers had only recently been given. Opponents of a large ICBM program pointed out that the major difficulty with ICBMs, how to aim them over very long distances with any assurance of accuracy, was still far from solved. But Schriever was making progress with his rocket's power; the Air Force's proposed Atlas ICBM would soon be able to hurl an atomic bomb over to Russia, but there was still a twenty-mile margin of error when it came to hitting specific targets. Schriever took a novel approach to eliminating that as a problem. He approached H-bomb mathematician John von Neumann and physicist Edward Teller and asked them to determine if the new H-bomb could be made light and compact enough to fit into the nose cone of an Atlas ICBM. Given the incredible range of destruction of hydrogen fusion warheads inside the missile, the missile's accuracy became much less important.

In 1953, Teller and Von Neumann joined with Schriever, Trevor Gardner (the Air Force undersecretary for Research and Development), and scientists Simon Ramo and Dean Woolridge as members of the Air Force's Strategic Missile Evaluation Committee. The Von Neumann Committee, as it came to be known, played a major role in pushing America to start an intercontinental missile program. The committee determined that H-bombs could be made small and light without sacrificing power and could be rocketed to the Soviet Union using available technology. The Atomic Energy Commission quickly promised to produce and test the H-bombs the committee had postulated. General Dynamic's Convair, which had held the research and development contract for long-range missiles with the Air Force since 1946, proposed a crash program of missile production. General Electric demonstrated a nose cone that would keep the new missiles from burning up on reentry. And two members of the committee, Simon Ramo and Dean Woolridge, joined together to form the Ramo Woolridge Company, which then bid for and received the contract for overall integration of the Air Force's ICBM program.

Eisenhower's Defense Department accepted the recommendations of the Von Neumann Committee and raised the nation's missile programs to the status of top priority. However, the department still maintained budget ceilings on these programs short of what missile promoters believed was necessary. General Schriever was given charge over all Air Force missile and space activity in 1954. The Army, over objections from the Air Force, which believed "flying rockets" ought to be their domain, established the Army Ballistic Missile Agency (ABMA) at the Redstone Arsenal. Von Braun's rocketeers worked there under ABMA commander General Medaris. The Navy continued its ongoing work on long-range missiles fired from submarines.

The missile competition, particularly between the Army and Air Force, became an intense and heated rivalry, which gradually grew bitter. By 1955 the competition spilled over into the public eye. The Air Force and Army exchanged accusations that year before congressional hearings on the state of America's missile development. General Medaris publicly accused top Air Force brass, and General Schriever specifically, of attempting to conceal and withhold valuable technological data from the Army by delays, bureaucratic obstruction, and outright refusal to share information. The conflict was a severe embarrassment to the Eisenhower administration: After all, the services were supposed to be working against the Soviet threat, not each other. It was evident that the Soviets were nearing an ICBM capability. In June 1955 the Soviet Academy of Sciences announced that it intended to launch an earth-orbiting satellite as part of its participation in the International Geophysical Year research program being planned for 1957. The announcement perturbed military circles. Rockets capable of launching satellites into orbit could just as well launch bombs across the oceans. The implication of the announcement was that the Soviets would soon have ICBMs.

President Eisenhower, in an attempt to avoid competition in intercontinental missiles, undertook a new arms control initiative with the specific purpose of banning intercontinental missiles on both sides. It was the first attempt to ban a new weapon before it was deployed. As part of his proposal, Eisenhower suggested both nations tolerate reconnaissance overflights by the other in order to verify compliance with the agreement. Much of the world, already horrified by the buildup of weapons and daily more aware of the nuclear fallout contaminating the atmosphere after nearly ten years of testing, looked at Eisenhower's proposals as a sign of hope.

The Soviet Union announced that it was prepared to agree to a ban on intercontinental ballistic missiles, but only as part of an agreement that included the intermediate-range ballistic missiles the United States had begun to place in Western Europe. The United States should also withdraw from its forward military bases in Europe and Asia, where American B-bombers stood poised with bellies full of bombs. The Soviets would not agree to reconnaissance overflight while America had missiles and bombers ready to strike Soviet targets. Such reconnaissance, they maintained, would be used to locate Soviet defenses and map potential targets.

But the United States would not give up its military superiority, nor would it consider arms control without adequate means of verification. The Soviets' rigidly controlled and highly centralized society would be much more able to act unilaterally and secretly than would the Americans, with their comparatively open access to information. Soviet secrecy, maintained by a police state, was frequently viewed by the U.S. military as a strength to be imitated and undermined if possible. Nothing came of Eisenhower's proposal to ban ICBMs, but reconnaissance overflight and "open skies" entered the vocabulary of arms control.

In 1956, despite the failure to agree on an open skies policy, the United States, in clear violation of international law, began reconnaissance overflights by secret CIA airplanes flying high above the range of Soviet antiaircraft guns. As it was clear to the Pentagon that Soviet antiaircraft capability would eventually reach the 60,000-feet flight altitude of the U-2 spyplanes, work was hastened on a spy satellite to replace the U-2.

The RAND Corporation studies in 1946 had acknowledged the feasibility of spying from space, but Air Force study projects on spy satellites never received enough funding to proceed beyond preliminary research. In 1951, another RAND study specifically focused on reconnaissance. In 1954, the year Eisenhower gave the go-ahead for the development of the U-2 program, the Air Force released a study reemphasizing the feasibility and utility of a satellite program for reconnaissance, intelligence gathering and meteorology. With the Air Force Atlas rocket program well under way, the Air Force gave out its first secret contracts for their projected reconnaissance satellites. Lockheed began work on the satellite itself; Eastman-Kodak and CBS would provide the cameras

At the same time rockets were being prepared to launch intercontinental missiles and spy satellites, scientists with the National Academy of Sciences urged the United States to launch a scientific research satellite as part of its participation in the International Geophysical Year (IGY).

The IGY was intended to unite the work of scientists around the world who were studying the earth as a geophysical unit through use of rockets, radar, and advanced optical instruments. A group of these scientists had gotten together in the early fifties and suggested the organization of a huge research project during which earth phenomena—such as weather patterns, ocean currents, and ionospheric conditions—could be recorded simultaneously from many different points on the globe. It would be the first attempt to study global patterns. Instruments flown aboard satellites capable of radioing their results back to earth would be tools to learn about an environment never before approached as a whole. The group proposed that a research program be undertaken under the auspices of the International Council of Scientific Unions. By 1953, planning for the International Geophysical Year was under way. It was a year that would last for eighteen months, from July 1957 through December 1958.

The National Academy of Sciences adopted a proposal for U.S. participation in the IGY that included the firing of numerous rockets into the upper atmosphere, as well as the launching of America's first satellite into space. The U.S. National Security Council (NSC) took up the issue of participation in IGY activities. The NSC was also concerned about the military implications of geophysical research. Information about the upper atmosphere and ionosphere would affect intercontinental missile design, and the popular interest sure to be aroused by satellites might jeopardize the secrecy surrounding early military plans for the use of space. Furthermore, the rules of the IGY required that all information gathered as part of its activities be shared with all other participating nations. The National Security Council decided that major IGY projects should be under the control of the Pentagon. The issue of freedom of passage in space was very much on the minds of both the National Security Council and the president. The mechanics of earth orbital flight would not allow much maneuverability outside strict orbital paths. There would be no way to avoid passing over the heads of friends and enemies alike. If the nations of the world were going to allow space flight at all, they would have to acquiesce to the reality of earth orbit and accept satellite overflight of their territories. "Open skies" with a clear view of the Soviet Union would then become a de facto reality in space.

President Eisenhower called a series of special conferences to determine the question of territoriality in space. No nation had ever laid claim to any region of space, and no current international law applied. Member nations of the IGY agreed to tolerate peaceful earth satellites passing over their territories. With this assurance the president himself went before the American people one month after the Soviets had made a similar announcement to say that the United States was undertaking the task of launching a satellite into space. The announcement received extensive press coverage. The Space Age was at hand, and the nation anxiously awaited a new era of adventure.

3

Sputnik and Military Strategy

America's IGY satellite effort was not the only satellite project being pursued by American scientists, but it was the only one of which the public was aware. Even as attention was focused on Eisenhower's announcement that the United States would launch a research satellite in cooperation with the IGY, the armed forces secretly pursued the development of satellites for military purposes. The president believed that military space objectives should receive highest priority. He also believed, however, that the United States should *appear* to be interested in outer space for strictly peaceful purposes. This conflict between appearances and reality complicated government decisions on how the early space program should be structured.

After the United States and the Soviet Union had each made its satellite intentions known, the IGY grew in importance. World leaders discussed the implications of space flight in their foreign affairs offices and at international forums. A new field, space law, was born. An international consensus emerged that rejected the idea of extending state sovereignty into space above national territories. Instead, the consensus favored ensuring that space be used exclusively for peaceful, scientific purposes. Only international agreements to reserve space for peaceful purposes could protect national security in the absence of sovereign rights. Both the United States and the Soviet Union publicly joined in the international consensus and both proclaimed that their space efforts would be for the "benefit of all mankind." Both sides also agreed to abide by IGY regulations, which obligated participants to make all information gathered during the IGY available to the international scientific community. It was widely believed that an open flow of information would prevent any nation from exploiting IGY research for military advantage.

The sad fact of the Space Age is that the opportunity to evolve a truly international space program was lost right at the beginning. Both the Soviet and American space plans, officially linked to a cooperative

program of international scientific research, succumbed to the nationalism, fear, competition, and militarism that marked the Cold War.
According to cold war mentality, any U.S. activity in space was by
American definition peaceful. By the same token, any Soviet activity in
space, whatever the purpose, was by definition warlike. Similar biases
distorted the thinking of Soviet leaders as well. The United States had a
strong interest in the exploitation of earth-orbiting satellites for such
service purposes as reconnaissance, early warning, communication,
and navigation. However, the Eisenhower administration placed a nonmilitary cover over America's space plans and conscientiously maintained a distance between the rockets being built for satellite launch and
those designed for ICBMs. Eisenhower hoped to negotiate a ban on
ICBMs. He did not want the space race to complicate the missile race.
On the other hand, the Soviet Union was particularly interested in
ICBMs as a means to balance American superiority in long-range bombardment capability. They saw it as in their interests to exaggerate their
missile capabilities. They made no effort to hide the link between
satellite launch and ICBMs.

American public perception of the two nations' early space ventures
was that the Soviet space program was carried out in secret with aggressive military intentions, whereas America pursued space activities in the
open for peaceful scientific purposes. Things were not that clear-cut.
The myths that continue to surround the history of the Space Age were
carefully manipulated by both sides for specific military and political
advantages. By the mid-1950s the United States was considerably ahead
of the Soviet Union in those areas of space technology with near-term
military applications. There is no evidence that the Soviet Union had,
or was developing, equivalent military capabilities. The Soviets' early
space work focused on the long-range goals of manned space flight. Its
military function was not to use satellites for specific military purposes,
but rather to test and demonstrate Soviet ICBM capability. The absence
of a specifically military space program allowed them to create a highly
organized rocket and space program. It eventually led to the appearance
of superiority that occurred in the late 1950s and early 1960s. In contrast, the United States, partly due to its technological wealth and
abundant military space development projects, found it extremely difficult to organize a national space program. Eisenhower attempted to
deal with the problem of organization in the IGY satellite project.

To keep attention on the peaceful, scientific aspects of U.S. space activities and to avoid interfering with the early military work, Eisenhower assigned the task of designing and managing the IGY satellite project to the National Academy of Sciences. The NAS would use the Naval Research Laboratory's Viking rocket, a workhorse that had been used frequently over the years in upper-atmospheric research. The joint NAS/NRL effort was named Project Vanguard. Those involved in the project were explicitly instructed not to interfere with any other missile or rocket program currently underway.

By choosing Project Vanguard over competing proposals made by the Army and the Air Force for launching an IGY satellite, the Eisenhower administration chose against haste in a space race with the Soviets. That decision was made for a variety of reasons, including a desire to have the Soviets establish the precedent of satellite overflight, to deflect attention away from ongoing military satellite preparations, and to avoid aggravating Army–Air Force rivalries. The NRL's Viking, a civilian rocket, had received much less attention and money than the Army's Jupiter and the Air Force's Atlas, either one of which, given the assignment and the necessary funding, could have sent an American satellite into space before Sputnik.

Long before the first satellite ever orbited the earth, it was becoming apparent that an arms race in space would be even more expensive and uncontrollable than the missile race. By the mid-fifties there were already developmental projects ranging from communications satellites to manned orbiting bombers, from navigation satellites to Air Force bases on the moon, from spy satellites to antisatellite weapons. The Eisenhower administration was trying to find some way to keep the burgeoning area of space projects under control. Emphasis was on assuring an orderly progression toward the two priority space items: reconnaissance satellites and early warning satellites. All three military services had, by 1956 and the beginning of Eisenhower's second term, initiated space programs focusing on everything from the technologically feasible to the naive, from the politically realistic to the blatantly provocative. The U.S. space effort seemed about to bubble over into an even bigger and more expensive mess than the many competing missile programs that had already disrupted administration economic policy, setting the services to even more intense squabbling with each other.

With all three services pursuing independent space programs, rivalry developed over which service would receive the most lucrative and exciting assignments. The Air Force insisted that it was the most logical choice to secure the new space environment for the nation, since air and space were indivisible, part of a continuum. A U.S. Space Force would simply be an Air Force flying ever higher. In 1955 the Air Force made its first of many requests officially to change its name to the U.S. Aerospace Force. Navy pitchmen waxed poetic about space being a new and uncharted sea. Spacecraft, after all, were commonly referred to as space*ships*. The Army didn't argue. They owned Von Braun and the V-2 team and had the most powerful rockets around.

Even the Atomic Energy Commission joined the fray. Fearful that U.S. research priorities were about to shift away from atomic energy to space research, the AEC established its own space program. The intention was to encourage the development of nuclear reactors for satellite power and nuclear rockets for propulsion.

By 1957 the desires of space militarists threatened to undermine Eisenhower's economic program and his foreign policy. In March the president offered another arms control initiative. Neither side had yet deployed intercontinental missiles or satellites. The United States proposed a total ban on what it called outer space weapons, by which it meant both intercontinental missiles that passed over the atmosphere and launching platforms in space for firing missiles down to earth.

Eisenhower's arms proposal claimed to be a means of assuring that outer space be reserved for peaceful purposes. It was the first time that the United States used the wording "space for peaceful purposes," which came to serve as a stock phrase for U.S. space intentions. As with Eisenhower's previous attempt to ban ICBMs, the Soviets insisted that the ban include U.S. intermediate-range missiles deployed by NATO within target range of the Soviet Union. And once again the United States refused to broaden the proposed ban. Intermediate-range missiles had become a crucial element in the new U.S. nuclear war plans.

In 1957 the Eisenhower-Dulles nuclear weapons strategy was receiving increasingly critical attention. U.S. military policy was based on the threat of an all-out nuclear attack in the event of Soviet expansion beyond the circle of containment defined by Truman. But many military and civilian strategists began to question the policy of massive retaliation. The criticisms took two forms.

One group, centered around Harvard professor Henry Kissinger at the Council on Foreign Relations, advised a shift in U.S. military doctrine toward limited, battlefield nuclear wars. They argued that an all-out nuclear attack was beyond the pale; simply too devastating to be considered. Because of that, America's nuclear capability was actually paralyzed by its very power. According to Kissinger, this left the Communists free to advance around the world in successive moves forward, each move too small to trigger a major nuclear response. "Massive retaliation" was an empty threat. In his widely read book, *Nuclear Weapons and Foreign Policy*, Kissinger argued for a strategy based on limited wars fought with short-range missiles and low-yield nuclear weapons under the control of a highly mobile, decentralized command.[1]

If adopted, a limited nuclear war strategy would have certain implications for U.S. missile and space policies. Less emphasis would be placed on ICBMs. Global communications, navigational aids for rapid mobility, and precise location of targets by satellite reconnaissance would all be valuable in limited nuclear war fighting. Soviet strategic thinking was also affected by America's public strategizing. For them, long-range missiles became even more important. America's limited nuclear wars would be fought in Europe, the Middle East, or Asia, on the Soviet borders and far from the United States. To virtually everyone but the Americans, a limited nuclear war would be catastrophic. The Soviets believed that only by warning American strategists that limited nuclear war would bring Soviet missiles across to the American mainland could such a war be avoided. They not only continued to build an ICBM capability while rejecting Eisenhower's proposal to ban "outer space weapons," but they also publicly boasted about their missile tests. Such boasts did not make Americans rest easy about Soviet intentions in space. American fears turned into public demands for an accelerated U.S. ICBM program.

In addition to Henry Kissinger and the Council on Foreign Relations, a group of strategists associated with the Air Force think tank, the RAND Corporation, also criticized America's nuclear strategy. They pointed out that America's threat to bomb Soviet population centers in the event of aggression by the Red Army was far less credible once the Soviets could retaliate in kind. Even if the Soviets succeeded only in delivering one thermonuclear weapon to one American city, the result would be devastating. Would the United States really risk New York to defend Berlin? The RAND strategists advised that America's war plans be changed. The United States should not unleash its entire arsenal in one assault. Rather, it should aim an initial strike at Soviet air bases, missile sites, and other military targets, while holding back a reserve nuclear force with which to deter the Soviets from responding with their surviving forces against American cities. If Soviet cities were spared, the reasoning went, then they would be more likely to spare American cities. Nuclear war could be fought according to civilized rules and ended by negotiation or victory.

RAND strategists also criticized America's reliance on overseas air bases from which to launch its nuclear-equipped bombers. Such bases, close to the Soviet Union, would be potentially vulnerable to a Soviet preemptive strike in advance of an invasion of Western Europe. Land-based ICBMs would be a back-up deterrence to compensate for the vulnerability of the Strategic Air Command's overseas bases. Therefore, ICBM development should be accelerated.

The RAND strategists' suggested changes in nuclear doctrine would, if adopted, affect missile and satellite development. Accurate targeting of Soviet military installations would require a significant improvement in the amount and quality of intelligence information over what was then available. The CIA's U-2 spy planes began overflight of Soviet territory in 1956. Satellite reconnaissance would be even more valuable for gathering information and mapping potential targets.

The critics of Eisenhower's strategy of massive retaliation against Soviet cities argued that the president was straitjacketed by this strategy into having only one option available in the event of war, and a horrifying option at that. They wanted to expand the president's options by preparing American forces for a number of different limited and controlled scenarios. Each new option would create new demands on technology. A direct link existed between nuclear strategy and technology requirements. But even more than this direct link between doctrine and hardware, there existed another factor driving the U.S. military toward the exploitation of near-earth space for military purposes. Conventional systems for military command and control communications and intelligence (C^3I) would be insufficient in the event of global thermonuclear war. Such a war would be so devastating, and would occur so quickly, over such large distances, that most war planners concluded it would surely be out of control. The only way to deal with nuclear war was to prevent one from ever starting. Space technology, however, held out the promise of some day being able to cope with the speeds, distances, and by being far above the action, the destructiveness of nuclear war. C³I systems based in space could potentially make nuclear war–fighting options more flexible. At the same time, the greater number of nuclear options would create a greater demand for C³I systems based in space. Thus, the development of space technology was closely linked to nuclear strategy. Throughout the history of the Space Age they remained inseparable.

In 1957, discussions of counterforce targeting and limited nuclear war were academic. They would remain so as long as the technology and force structure to limit and control nuclear warfare did not exist and the Soviets did not yet pose an intercontinental nuclear threat. But U.S. space technology was advancing, and the Soviets were rapidly approaching an ICBM capability. The space and missile race was on.

The first major event in the race occurred on August 26, 1957, when the Soviet Union announced it had successfully tested an ICBM. Two months and one week later, a Soviet rocket sent a 184-pound satellite, Sputnik I, into a five-hundred-mile-high orbit, traveling at eighteen thousand miles per hour. The performance of Sputnik's booster rocket, which itself attained orbital speed and visibly moved across the night sky, suggested that the Soviets could launch a powerful bomb, at very high speeds, to targets within a four-thousand-mile radius. Sputnik verified the basic mechanics of orbital flight, which until then had remained speculative. The Soviet satellite carried no scientific instruments, but it did transmit a radio signal that was received by amateur radio enthusiasts around the world.

Significantly, despite the wave of emotions stimulated worldwide by the event, not a single government anywhere in the world protested the fact that Sputnik had flown over their lands. The principle of "open skies," a long-sought-after objective of American arms control negotiators, was established by default. The precedent was set by the Soviets. The U.S. intelligence agencies and the Air Force took note. Although the Soviets might in the future object to satellite reconnaissance, there would be no way to determine which satellites carried cameras and/or radar detection devices and which ones did not. The right of peaceful passage had clearly been affirmed, and in truth virtually all passage could be made to appear peaceful.

The success of Sputnik created a domestic political situation that quickly got out of Eisenhower's control. The American people simply could not understand how the Soviets, universally feared as barbaric, could have beaten America's best scientists in the race to place an object into space. The president tried to reassure the American people that Sputnik had come as no surprise and would not affect current U.S. military or space programs. At a news conference five days after the successful launch of Sputnik I, President Eisenhower spoke to reporters with a nonchalance that was completely at odds with the way Americans were reacting to Sputnik. "Every scientist I have talked to since this occurred has spoken in most congratulatory terms about the capabilities of the Russian scientists in putting this thing in the air. They expressed themselves as pleased, rather than chagrined, because at least the Soviets have proved the first part of it—that this thing will successfully orbit." [2] To Americans, only recently barraged with the anti-Communist harangues of Joseph McCarthy and thoroughly familiar with Cold War ideology, Eisenhower's congratulations to Soviet scientists was incomprehensible.

Eisenhower's troubles were compounded by the release of a supposedly secret report written by an independent group of military analysts for the Defense Department. The Gaither Report, so named for the group's chairman, H. Rowan Gaither—he was also chairman of the Ford Foundation and of the RAND Corporation—suggested that by the early 1960s the Soviet Union would be well ahead of the United States in the deployment of long-range ballistic missiles. The report, entitled "Deterrence and Survival in the Nuclear Age," was released three days after Sputnik. It criticized the Eisenhower administration's budget ceilings on military spending and urged the adoption of a crash program to hasten the deployment of the missiles being developed by all three services.

The Gaither Committee Report's conclusions about Soviet missile strength were based on Air Force intelligence estimates. The Air Force frequently used such numbers to justify increases in the Air Force budget. Army, Navy, and CIA estimates of Soviet missile capacity were all considerably lower. The report suggested that if the Soviet Union chose to mobilize its productive capacity totally in pursuit of an ICBM capability, there might well be hundreds of Soviet ICBMs by the early sixties. The committee did not claim that the Soviets *intended* to turn their entire national physical plant to building missiles. Capacity, not intention, was discussed. And no measure of military strength other than ICBM strength was taken into account.

The report was not only concerned about Soviet missile strength, but also about American will. It urged that the American people be indoctrinated into a crisis mentality in order to accept the high taxes and reduced social services that permanently high military budgets would bring. The timing of the release of the report went a long way toward that indoctrination. Both President Eisenhower and Secretary of State Dulles termed the report and its release "irresponsible." But no amount of reassurance from Eisenhower could turn the tide. The coming missile gap was firmly placed in America's consciousness.

When the United States' first attempt to launch the Explorer satellite, whose softball dimensions and frail, light weight already compared unfavorably with Sputnik, failed in a launch-pad fire, the American press greeted the event with a wave of self-humiliation. Headlines referred to the debacle as Flopnik and Kaputnik. The failure of the Viking rocket led to the overturning of the original decision favoring Project Vanguard; the task of launching America's satellite was turned over to Von Braun and the Army Ballistic Missile Agency.

In December 1957 Russian scientists launched Sputnik II. It carried the first living creature, a dog, into earth orbit. The capsule that carried the animal weighed over a thousand pounds. As numerous American newspaper editorials pointed out, rockets powerful enough to carry a thousand pounds into orbit would certainly be able to carry Soviet nuclear weapons to New York, Chicago, San Francisco . . .

The United States could not match Soviet successes in launching heavy weights. Despite U.S. superiority in almost every area related to space technology, the United States did not have rockets capable of such a feat. The reason for the apparent inferiority was simply that the United States had not pursued the development of such large rockets because they served no immediate U.S. military purpose. Ever since the Atomic Energy Commission had shrunk the size of hydrogen warheads, U.S. rocket thrust requirements had been decreased. There was no need to build rockets to carry such heavy weights. Although work proceeded on developing powerful rockets for future launches of space vehicles, the priority given large booster rockets was low compared to the priority given to the rockets and materials for ICBMs. But now the Army Ballistic Missile Agency and Von Braun's V-2 team received the assignment to catch up with Soviet large booster rocket capability. A panic was building across the nation, much of it purposely encouraged by people who had something to sell or something to gain. The press searched for answers as to why America had been defeated, but few looked in the right places. An article entitled "Arguing the Case for Being Panicky" appeared in *Life* magazine, claiming that "unless we depart utterly from our present behavior it is reasonable to expect that by no later than 1975 the US will be a member of the USSR.[3] The Democratic party leadership, seeing a potential winning presidential election issue, played up the sense of crisis. "Let us not fail to understand that control of outer space would be a military fact of the highest importance," read a Democratic policy statement signed by former President Truman, Governor Averell Harriman of New York, and Senators Adlai Stevenson and Hubert Humphrey. The statement went on to warn that "the air war of yesterday becomes the space war of tomorrow. We must do more than merely catch up. The all-out effort of the Soviets to establish themselves as masters of space around us must be met by all-out efforts of our own."[4] Senator Lyndon Johnson, chairman of the powerful Senate Preparedness Investigating Subcommittee (which had repeated and amplified the Gaither Committee charges), and already running for the presidency on the hopes and fears stimulated by the Space Age, also took up the issue. In a political speech, he asserted that "control of space means control of the world, far more certainly, far more totally than any control that has been achieved by weapons or by troops of occupation. Space is the ultimate position, the position of total control over Earth."[5]

Eisenhower was trapped. Although the administration was confident that Soviet rockets posed no near-term threat, he couldn't reveal the U-2 spyplanes on which U.S. information about Soviet capabilities depended. Nor could he discuss the actual state of U.S. missile and space programs without revealing military secrets. His was a difficult position endemic to a decision-making process based on secret information available only to an anointed few. His critics could make all sorts of wild claims that would be as credible as any other speculation, because the truth was highly classified.

On January 16, 1958, under growing public pressure to meet the Soviet challenge, President Eisenhower abandoned all hope of achieving a balanced federal budget. He sent to Congress the largest peacetime military budget in the nation's history up to that time. And yet, in every single military category, Congress voted to increase the amount above the president's request. When Admiral Burke claimed that the greatest Soviet threat came not from missiles fired from space, but from missiles launched from beneath the sea, Congress voted to increase his budget for Polaris submarine-launched missiles. The allocations for long-range ballistic missiles and Air Force space research and development swelled the Air Force budget alone to an unprecedented $19.7 billion, 26 percent of the entire federal budget.

The House Science and Astronautics Committee outlined a missile and space strategy the committee believed America should undertake to maintain national security. The House recommended that all four major American missile programs be accelerated and expanded, that powerful rockets with one million pounds of thrust be developed to carry large platforms into space, that research and development begin on an antiballistic missile system capable of defending against Russian ICBMs, and that work should begin on what the committee called "manned missiles"—manned spacecraft.

It was boomtime in the aerospace industry. Political pressure was on the government to buy what the industry had to sell. The sudden rush of space and missile contracts coincided with a rise in demand for new jet airplanes for domestic airlines as a result of the new popularity of passenger flight. The combination stimulated the blossoming of a powerful industry with growing political and economic clout in California, Texas, Oklahoma, Missouri, and Washington—an industry that came to employ fully 20 percent of the nation's entire population of scientists, engineers, and technicians.

Money began to pour in for space and missile research and development, but there was as yet no coordination of decisions and priorities among the limitless technological possibilities forwarded for countering the Soviet threat. Realizing this, Eisenhower and the Defense Department moved to give coherence to government policies on science and technology. Eisenhower established the President's Science Advisory Committee (PSAC) and appointed James Killian its first chairman. The Committee on Government Organization was formed to recommend to the president ways of organizing the huge new government programs. Nelson Rockefeller was named to head the committee. It immediately recommended that the U.S. space program be centralized under the control of a single agency. The Defense Department created the Defense Advanced Research Projects Agency and assigned it the coordination of the space research and development going on separately under the three military services.

It was anticipated that the services would defend their space turf against the powerful new agency. The Air Force in particular was concerned that the Defense Advanced Research Projects Agency (DARPA) would become a fourth service and eventually take over the Space Force role coveted by the Air Force. To forestall any such power struggle, DARPA was prevented at its formation from entering into any contracts of its own with corporate suppliers. The ultimate power of the contract purse remained with the services. DARPA would decide what research and development projects should be pursued; the services would administer and contract out these projects. DARPA initiated a long list of military space programs immediately after Sputnik.

Von Braun's team successfully launched the United States' first Explorer satellite on January 31, 1958. The Soviets quickly followed with a shot that took a spaceship close to and past the moon. Catching and passing the Soviets became a national obsession. The immediate legacy of Sputnik and Explorer was a period of sword rattling, anti-Communist blustering, and widespread anxiety and fear that someday soon nuclear devastation would be unleashed from the heavens.

4

The Early Military Plans

Two months prior to the first successful test of a Soviet ICBM and five months before Sputnik, in June 1957, America's first official attempted firing of a long-range guided missile ended in a misfire. The second attempt, in September, failed as well. But on December 17 the third Air Force Atlas ICBM test vehicle was successfully launched and guided for several hundred miles to its target. By the late 1950s, both the United States and the Soviet Union were on the brink of deploying intercontinental ballistic missiles.

In both countries the testing and further development of rockets for ICBMs were the major purposes of early space activity. According to General Hollingsworth Gregory, commander of the Air Force Office of Scientific Research, writing in *Missiles and Rockets* magazine, it was logical that "the Air Force, when the ICBMs become operational, will want to train their launching crews and test their vehicles under realistic conditions; and a good way to do it might well be to send modified versions of these vehicles into orbit around the moon."[1] Since the sole purpose of ICBMs is to make possible the waging of global nuclear war, they couldn't very well be used regularly. In addition, testing a missile with a range of thousands of miles presented the risk of accidents in distant lands, with resulting international complications. The complex rockets, with their internal guidance systems, were perishable by nature and would deteriorate if left unused. They could, on the other hand, be regularly tested and improved by shooting them off into space. It was the desire to upgrade and test ICBM rockets that created most of the early military interest in space flight. And the exploitation of near-earth space for improved intelligence gathering and military communications was what led to the early interest in earth-orbiting satellites. No doubt the longing for adventure and the quest for knowledge played their parts in opening the Space Age too. But in 1958, as today, the drive to understand the universe, to explore the planets, and to soar off into the galaxies was decidedly secondary (although it was publicly touted to influence the populace).

Since 1955 the announced goal of the Soviet space program was manned space travel. They pursued dramatic goals that would demonstrate technical proficiency and military potential, thereby lending national prestige. In so doing they paid less attention to space activities with near-term scientific, commercial, or military usefulness and more to those that involved long-term goals and national prestige. In contrast, the United States divided its energies among a number of different space efforts. The many interests involved in early space activities could not agree on goals or purposes. By 1958 the Army, Navy, and especially the Air Force all had a wide range of ongoing space research and development projects.

In addition to ICBM rocket development, the highest priority went to satellites that would provide support services for an ICBM force. An operational ICBM force requires supporting satellites for geodesy, weather surveillance, targeting, early warning of enemy missiles, intelligence gathering about enemy radar defense, and continuous surveillance. Closest to actual deployment was a set of Air Force satellites known as Weapon System 117-L. It consisted of three separate programs: Discoverer, SAMOS, and MIDAS. The Discoverer satellites were designed to demonstrate the feasibility of photographic reconnaissance from space. The RAND Corporation had carried out a series of design studies on reconnaissance satellites under the name Project Feedback in 1952 and 1953. In 1956 the first Air Force contracts for reconnaissance satellite hardware were granted. After Sputnik, the Air Force satellite program was accelerated. Involved were Lockheed, Eastman-Kodak, and CBS labs. The early Discoverer satellites would be concerned with research and development on various photographic reconnaissance techniques. Cameras aboard Discoverer satellites would eject their exposed film in protective capsules into the atmosphere. Various methods of retrieving the reentry capsules were pursued. Eventually, a technique of mid-air pick-up by specially designed retriever airplanes was perfected. The early Discoverer satellites proved to be enormously successful. They provided pictures to be transformed into detailed maps of every square inch of Soviet territory.

The SAMOS (Satellite Missile Observation System) satellites were designed to work in cooperation with the Discoverer satellites. When operational, they would carry cameras with far wider surveillance coverage than the Discoverer cameras but produce less detailed pictures. They would fly at higher altitudes and therefore would stay in orbit for much longer periods of time before they burned up in the atmosphere. SAMOS cameras would peer down for three to four weeks at a time, transmitting photographic data via radio relay to special ground stations. If the SAMOS cameras revealed something that piqued the interest of the intelligence analysts, a Discoverer satellite would be sent up for a three- to four-day, low-altitude mission to get a closer, more detailed look. Technologically more sophisticated than the Discoverer series, SAMOS would not begin operations until 1961, two years after the start of Discoverer flights.

The third element in Weapon System 117-L was known as MIDAS (Missile Defense Alarm System). MIDAS was designed to cope with one of the most frightening aspects of ICBMs, their tremendous speed. Without early warning from space, by the time land-based radar spotted an incoming ICBM barrage there would be precious little time to prepare or respond. MIDAS would be the first attempt to provide space-based warning systems. By constantly scanning the atmosphere above Soviet territory for the telltale infrared signature of ICBM booster rocket exhaust, and immediately transmitting a warning to American defenses at the first sign of attack, crucial minutes could be gained during a nuclear crisis. MIDAS was even more technologically difficult than SAMOS. Early work on MIDAS would focus on demonstrating the feasibility of detecting infrared radiation with sensors in space.

In 1958, Navy scientists under the auspices of the Defense Advanced Research Projects Agency (DARPA), were developing Transit, America's first satellite-based navigation system. Transit's basic concept was simple. Through calculations of the time it takes to receive signals from two Transit satellites of known distance from each other, a navigator on any appropriately equipped ship, plane or surface vehicle would be able to determine his latitude and longitude with much greater precision than with conventional navigational aids. Increased navigational precision would also improve the accuracy of submarine-launched missiles. Therefore, Transit would eventually make the Navy capable of matching the accuracy of the Air Force's land-based ICBMs and long-range bombers and thereby hasten the Polaris submarine's rise in strategic importance.

The Army had its pet satellite projects as well. Under DARPA, Army scientists worked on Project Score, the nation's first communications satellite. Score was designed to be a passive device, a simple foil-covered orbiting globe that would deflect and scatter signals back to earth. The Navy was carrying out similar communications research using the moon to bounce off signals linking Washington with naval bases in the South Pacific. The Army was also exploring the possibility of establishing a global communications linkup involving satellites in geostationary orbit. A geostationary satellite is one that orbits the earth at the equator every twenty-four hours. In effect, it remains stationary with respect to any given point on earth. As a result, ground transmitters and receivers can remain pointed at the same place in the sky and be assured of maintaining line-of-sight contact with the satellite. If four communications satellites were placed in stationary orbit around the earth approximately ninety degrees apart from each other, then continuous communications between any two points on earth could be maintained. Stationary satellites would revolutionize military C^3I by making instantaneous global communications possible. Bombers, submarines, troops, and spacecraft all around the world might one day all be controlled from a single command center. Such a geostationary system would require lifting large satellites to positions twenty-two thousand miles above the earth. In 1958, the Army was still a long way from having rockets with the necessary power. But Von Braun and his V-2 team were vigorously working on such powerful rockets with Project Advent, the Army's geostationary communications satellite project, in mind.

The Army had its own surveillance satellite project, in direct competition with the Air Force. It would be similar to the Air Force's SAMOS. TIROS (Television and Infra-Red Observation Satellite) was conceived as the Army's real-time surveillance satellite for battlefield reconnaissance. Later, when the Air Force officially received the space reconnaissance assignment from the Department of Defense, TIROS became the U.S. military's weather surveillance system, under the name NIMBUS.

Geodetic satellites that measure variations in the curvature of the earth and the resulting gravitational anomalies would also assist in improving the accuracy of ICBMs and submarine-launched missiles. The Navy and DARPA had begun work on such systems for geodetic research, under Project ANNA.

Taken together, all of these satellite projects—the Air Force's Discoverer, SAMOS, and MIDAS; the Army's Score, Advent, and TIROS; the Navy's Transit and ANNA—summed up what could be done in space with unmanned satellites carrying various kinds of sensors, receivers, and transmitters. Each aimed at exploiting the advantage of an overview of the earth's surface from out in space—gathering, transmitting, and relaying various kinds of information valuable for earth-based military tasks. Because these first military satellites would not be armed, America's public posture that space be reserved for peaceful, scientific pursuits would not necessarily be compromised by their development. And because they would be unmanned, their development would not attract widespread public attention. But their development, and later, their successful deployment, made near-earth space a region of critical military importance. Military leaders were faced with a future where space vehicles would play increasingly crucial roles. They began planning for capturing and controlling space with an armed space force, not merely utilizing space. They debated the role of the military astronaut and considered design requirements for his spacecraft. According to the thinking prevalent around those early military space programs, the air battles of World War II would be the space battles of World War III. It only made sense to prepare for battle. Thus, despite America's acceptance of the international consensus that sought to reserve space for peaceful, scientific purposes, all three services and DARPA were pursuing a number of space weapons prospects at the inception of the Space Age.

The first requirement for an armed force is the ability to intercept and destroy enemy spacecraft in time of war. Antisatellite (ASAT) weapons would have technology requirements similar to antiballistic missile (ABM) weapons. In 1958, a great deal of effort was going into developing workable ABMs to counter the predicted Soviet missile threat. The most advanced ABM at the time was the Army's Nike-Zeus system, which was designed to intercept incoming ICBMs as they entered the upper atmosphere. Some of the Army's ABM work was steered toward developing ground-launched ASATs. Since satellites travel in highly predictable paths, the tracking and guidance demands of a direct-ascent, ground-launched ASAT would be simpler than the demands on an ABM. In addition, an ASAT could carry a large-yield nuclear weapon since no fallout danger would exist in space. By carrying nuclear weapons, with their wide destructive range (made even greater in space by the lack of an atmosphere to absorb any of its destructive power), the requirements for accuracy would be greatly reduced. But the Army's ground-launched ASAT would have one major drawback: it would be limited by the need to wait for the target satellite to enter an orbit that would carry it over the Army's ASAT launch site. The Navy pursued an ASAT weapon that would be rocketed from the deck of a ship. The ship could position itself in advance to where it could take aim at a target satellite. The Air Force promised even greater mobility with an air-launched ASAT to be fired into space by a high-flying jet. (This system, much improved, became the basis for the Air Force's ASAT for the 1990s.) The Air Force was also drawing up plans for an advanced ASAT that would go into orbit along with the target satellite, maneuver nearby, inspect it with cameras and other sensors, and destroy it if determined to be hostile.

ASATs would be weapons based on earth and aimed at objects in space. Weapons aimed in the opposite direction were also being considered. Ultimately, the greatest threat of the Space Age is always that a nation will fill the skies with nuclear-armed satellites and threaten to bring them down by command from earth. Shortly after Walter Dornberger's arrival in the United States in 1947, when he was working as a guided missile consultant for the U.S. Air Force, he wrote a paper describing a space bombardment system consisting of hundreds of nuclear bombs in orbit. In the 1950s, Air Force Project NABS (Nuclear Armed Bombardment Satellites) placed the possibility of such a system under study. The placement of offensive nuclear weapons in space would have severe political and military repercussions in international relations. However, defensive systems similar in concept might be more acceptable. Armed satellites to shoot down Soviet missiles as they rise from their launch pads were being considered under Air Force Project BAMBI (Ballistic Missile Booster Interceptors). (Project BAMBI was identical in concept to the space-based ballistic missile defense schemes that reemerged in the late 1970s, promoted by space militarists as an active defense system for the 1990s and the twenty-first century.)

Each of the many space projects that received funding in the 1950s had its partisans among the scientists, whose prestige was at stake; the officers, whose power would rise along with the budgets they controlled; the aerospace corporations, who were eager to cash in their study contracts for production orders; and members of Congress, whose political fortunes were frequently allied with the health of the military contractors at home. These special interests confused what was already a confusing decision-making process. Did America really want to enter an arms race in space? If not, how could one be avoided? Should the United States develop an offensive military capability, a defensive capability, or unarmed support systems only? What could the available technology support? What was affordable? Should the military develop a manned military capability? Should there be separate military and civilian space programs? As the nation entered the Space Age, there were many unanswered questions about what was possible in space, what was practical, affordable, and what would be in the best interests of the American people. In the absence of long-term space goals, the Eisenhower administration was incapable of answering the fundamental questions about America's future in space. And so America's many space projects developed blindly, pushed forward by the force of competing interests.

In the early days of America's space effort a major debate raged over the value of space pilots. Carrying an astronaut into space would mean carrying along thousands of pounds in life-support equipment. Manned spacecraft would be far more costly to design and operate than instrumented satellites. Given the uncertainty over whether a human could even survive in space, instrumented satellites would do as well as piloted spacecraft for those few tasks that had near-term military value: navigation aid, geodesy, communications relay, early warning, and, less clearly, reconnaissance. But many officers in the early military space programs, particularly those connected with Dyna-Soar—the Air Force's reusable, manned aerospace glider—argued that military astronauts would one day be as indispensable to the nation as Air Force pilots were at the time. On manned reconnaissance missions astronauts could pick and choose where to point their cameras. The kind of controlled reentry that would be required of an aerospace bomber would be inconceivable without a pilot on board. As a study done for the President's Science Advisory Committee in 1958 put it, "Manned space vehicles offer a logical extension of our deterrent capability. Such a system holds promise of providing, for the first time, a carrier vehicle equivalent in sophistication to atomic weapons."[2]

Two further arguments pointed most convincingly in favor of a manned space effort. First, the Soviets had publicly stated that manned space travel was the goal of their space program. The orbiting of a dog in a space capsule in November 1957 demonstrated their interest in space biology experimentation. There was convincing evidence that the Soviets intended to orbit a man in a larger version of the same capsule that carried Laika, the space dog. It was even more evident that they possessed rockets of sufficient power to lift a manned spacecraft by the early 1960s. A Soviet manned space program in the absence of an American counterpart would be seen as a serious blow to America's international prestige. A president who allowed such a situation to occur would not be popular with the voters. Second, manned space travel had the potential to arouse mass public interest and support of the nation's overall space program. Popular support was going to be essential. Conquering space would be a long-term and very expensive endeavor.

Even after presidential approval was granted to a manned space effort, a choice had to be made between competing space vehicle concepts. There were two manned space vehicles being developed cooperatively by the Air Force and the National Advisory Council on Aeronautics (NACA). NACA had been doing the nation's advanced research in aircraft design since World War I. Whenever NACA developed an experimental craft to the point where it could be tested, it was turned over to the appropriate service for decisions about its future production. Project Mercury, America's first space capsule, was under NACA's auspices before the establishment of NASA. Mercury was intended to be a first-step research craft designed to test how well a person would survive actual rocket flight. The Mercury capsule was more a modified ICBM nose cone than a spacecraft. The astronaut would sit inside the reentry vehicle, where the bomb would normally go. A true spacecraft, Air Force planners believed, would be an advanced version of the rocket-launched gliders the Air Force had been testing for some time in the upper atmosphere.

The earliest aerospace glider concept came out of the work of the German rocket scientists in World War II. They had proposed a glide bomber that would skip over the top of the atmosphere. When General

Dornberger went to work for the Bell Aviation company he brought with him his studies on aerospace glide bombers. Bell was already building the Air Force's fastest research planes. They proposed to the Air Force a study series based on Dornberger's ideas and received a contract for Project ROBO (Rocket Bomber).

Bell's high-speed, high-altitude research planes were among the Air Force's X series of planes that consistently shattered the outer limits of air flight. In 1947, the X-1 was the first airplane to break the sound barrier. In 1956, the X-2 flew to an altitude of 126,200 feet, effectively above the atmosphere. By 1958, the X-15 glider, rocket-launched from a B-52 in flight, was examining the conditions of a controlled glide in altitudes where air is scarce and aerodynamic lift and drag is absent. The next step would be attaining orbital velocity and reentering to a controlled landing in the X-20, also known as the Dyna-Soar (Dynamic Soaring). It was natural to assume that America's first operational manned spacecraft would be an Air Force X-20. If the Air Force was ever to achieve active control of space, then some form of maneuverable, reusable spaceplane would be required. To the officers in charge of Dyna-Soar, NACA's Project Mercury was merely a space medicine experiment. The Dyna-Soar would be a real spacecraft. But for a number of complex technological, political, and economic reasons, Dyna-Soar was not to be. It would eventually lumber through a decade of development before being canceled. It would later reemerge in improved form as the U.S. Space Shuttle.

Most of the early space plans focused on instrumented satellites in low-earth orbit. But for many, the moon beckoned as the most likely and important goal. From a military point of view, the moon appeared to be less vulnerable, more defensible, than manned space stations or satellites. Among the most ambitious space projects in 1958 was an early plan for establishing a base on the moon. Project Lunex was undertaken by the Air Force Office of Advanced Technology under its director, General Homer Boushey. Boeing Aircraft, Douglas Aircraft, North American Aviation, General Electric, and the Honeywell Corporation all received contracts to draw up plans for transportation of materials to the moon, with subsequent construction and operation of a moon base.

General Boushey became a vocal spokesman for what he saw as the military advantages of the moon. According to Boushey, the moon would be ideal as a missile base. Missile guidance would be facilitated by the fact that launch crews on the moon could observe and guide a missile along its entire flight path, unlike on earth, where a missile's trajectory takes it behind the horizon. The dark side of the moon could be an ideal place to conceal activities such as missile construction and space weapons tests. The moon's moderate gravitation would make moon-to-earth bombardment simpler than earth-to-moon retaliation. And finally, arming the moon would avoid the international political consequences that would be the expected result of armed American space stations and satellites, which would necessarily cross over the exposed homelands of friends and enemies alike. [3]

General Boushey, his corporate supporters among the space contractors, and others, such as H-bomb scientist Edward Teller, who supported the moon base, argued for haste in building a moon-traveling capability. As one general put it, "I would hate to think that the Russians got to the moon first. The first nation that does will probably have a tremendous military advantage over any potential enemy." [4] The fact that the Soviets' third space shot, Lunik, flew past the moon gave the Air Force moon men a strong sense of urgency.

At the opening of the Space Age the nation still had no way of choosing among the many possible paths the American space effort could travel. Should it focus on the moon, or near-earth space? Should the emphasis be on manned or unmanned spacecraft, prestige or practicality? Should it be secret or public, military or civilian controlled? Should the Air Force be in charge, should space tasks be divided among the services, or should they combine in a joint command? The president wanted to avoid the interservice rivalries and political machinations that had plagued the nation's missile programs. Toward that end he had asked the Defense Department to establish an agency within the Pentagon to bring some centralized control to the numerous space projects in the various services. On February 7, 1958, the Defense Advanced Research Projects Agency (DARPA) was established in response to the president's request and given overall responsibility for the nation's space program. However, under DARPA's first administrator, Roy Johnson, the agency not only failed to bring coherence to space research, but it deliberately encouraged some of the more outlandish spacehawk fantasies.

Roy Johnson had been appointed DARPA administrator by Secretary of Defense Neil McElroy, Eisenhower's replacement for Defense Secretary Charles Wilson, who had died in office. Johnson came to DARPA from a career in the advertising department of General Electric's Appliance Division. An unremarkable talent, he had climbed the ladder of success at GE by being fiercely loyal to GE's powerful president, Ralph Cordiner. Neil McElroy, Johnson's boss at the Defense Department, a former member of the board of directors of General Electric, also came to the Eisenhower administration from a career in advertising, his with Proctor & Gamble.

Johnson became one of the space hawks' most outspoken advocates. He was a frequent witness at congressional hearings on the nation's space future and regularly testified with a bellicose candor that was embarrassing and unacceptable to the White House. A confusion of roles and authority erupted between Johnson at DARPA and Herbert York, the Defense Department's director of Research and Engineering, who took a much more restrained approach toward developing space for military purposes.

Johnson publicly proclaimed DARPA's goal to be the establishment of U.S. supremacy in the region he considered military space—between the earth and the moon. Among his pet fantasies was a system for lifting huge, armed space stations into orbit using a cluster of atomic explosives grouped beneath a gigantic lifting platform. As Johnson explained to a congressional hearing, "This is quite a trick. First of all, you use little bombs, and you use a lot of them. The trick is the creation of a spring mechanism on the platform. This is a peculiar thing; it won't work with anything little like a hundred tons; it has got to be real big or it won't work, and it has a springing device, against which the shock waves thrust, driving the vehicle. Of course the shock must be absorbed sufficiently so that the inhabitants of it are not killed but so that thrust is still obtained."[5] Johnson initiated a unique contracting system under DARPA's Project Longsight, which invited companies to demonstrate that some weapons concepts were *not* feasible. It was up to the contractors what they wished to disprove. Under Longsight, contracts were awarded for the study of radar death rays, antigravity and antimatter weapons, magnetic missile shields in space, and particle beam weapons, all as possible antiballistic missile systems. Under Johnson's unlimited imagination and his unique administration, it remained impossible to distinguish which of the many military space proposals were technologically plausible and which were but fantasies.

One project DARPA carried out was a direct result of the discovery of the Van Allen radiation belts by instruments aboard America's first orbiting satellite, Explorer, at the beginning of 1958.

In the midst of all the turmoil surrounding Sputnik and Explorer, most observers forgot about the scientific missions satellites were ostensibly launched to perform. Instruments aboard the early Explorer satellites transmitted some remarkable information to earth about conditions in space. James Van Allen, an astrophysicist at the University of Iowa, designed the instrumentation that flew aboard Explorers I and II to measure the levels of radiation in the regions of space the satellite would traverse. The Explorer satellites discovered that the earth is surrounded by belts of high-energy atomic particles trapped by the earth's magnetic field. By recording the fluctuations in the levels of radiation intensity in the Van Allen Belt, as it came to be known, scientists could map the strength and shape of the earth's magnetic field extending out into space.

Meanwhile, in America's secret military labs, scientists were busily studying the data and considering its implications for military space activities. If the earth's magnetic field trapped and concentrated cosmic radiation, what would it do with the radiation released by an atomic explosion? Could the radiation belt be augmented or diminished at will? What effects would tampering with the radiation belts have on antiballistic missiles, spacecraft, and military communications? These questions led to the decision that DARPA would coordinate the secret detonation of atomic weapons in space, what some later would call the "boldest experiment in history."

5

Project Argus:
Atomic Tests in Space

Somewhere in the universe an exploding star floods space with atomic debris. A powerful eruption on the surface of the sun scatters high-energy atomic particles across the length and breadth of the solar system. Solar particles and cosmic rays are captured by the earth's magnetism and formed into a belt of radiation that surrounds the earth with varying levels of intensity from about 500 to 40,000 miles altitude above the surface. The belt functions as a kind of shield in space, preventing solar particles and cosmic radiation from striking the surface of the planet, where they would raise havoc with life's reproductive biology. During periods of extreme solar activity with many solar flare eruptions, and at times when the planet passes through a particularly dense cloud of cosmic radiation, the quantity of captured particles in the Van Allen Belt rises significantly. At these times quantities of high-energy particles leak into the atmosphere at the geomagnetic poles, resulting in the colorful and mysterious auroras visible in both the northern and southern hemispheres.

The magnetic field is thrown out into space through the action of some gigantic dynamo of molten iron deep within the earth's core. Not all planets have strong magnetic fields and accompanying radiation belts. Earth and Jupiter do, Venus and Mars do not. The earth's magnetic field is in the same shape as a small magnetic field, the pattern you can see when you toss a handful of iron filings over a bar magnet. The field lines farthest from earth, which form the belt, surround the earth like the skin of an apple bending around and inward toward the stem, the poles.

Even today, the earth's magnetism is largely a mystery. The earth's electromagnetic field, with its many shifts and changes, has subtle and pervasive effects on all living things. But in 1958, when scientists designed the instruments that discovered the Van Allen Belt, they weren't thinking about arcane biological matters. In the psychological and ideological atmosphere of the times, the significant implications of magnetic fields and radiation belts for future military space activities were what drew the attention of the government's physicists.

Nicholas Christofilos, an eccentric, self-taught physicist-genius working at the University of California's Livermore Radiation Laboratories, developed techniques to harness and control the energy released in hydrogen fusion reactions. No known materials could contain the superhot plasmas involved. Christofilos was working on fashioning magnetic "bottles," powerful magnetic fields to hold the electrically charged plasma. Because of the nature of the shape of magnetic fields, a certain quantity of charged particles would leak out of the ends of the magnetic bottle, in much the same way that trapped particles leak out at the earth's poles, producing the auroras.

The launching of Sputnik I set Christofilos to thinking. Wouldn't the earth's magnetic field act the same way as the magnetic fields he generated in his lab? On January 10, 1958, he put his thoughts down on paper. If a nuclear weapon were exploded in space, the radioactive debris would be trapped and directed by the magnetic field, and the result would be the artificial creation of a band of relativistic electrons that would completely surround the earth. He speculated that this radiation belt could be made intense enough to destroy satellites in orbit. Future military astronauts might also face a situation where the enemy had rendered the region of near-earth space temporarily lethal with radioactivity. Furthermore, the belt would produce worldwide radio noise on the HF and VHF radio bands that carried the bulk of military communications. Most significantly, the explosion of a nuclear weapon in near-earth space could create artificial auroras, and increase the intensity of a chosen region of the ionosphere, rendering warning radar and antiballistic missile guidance systems useless and blacking out radio communications. By accurately calculating the site for an explosion, its effects could be made to occur over a specific target area. An artificial magnetic storm and aurora could be produced and used as an environmental weapon in advance of a surprise missile attack. Christofilos urged that the government test his postulates by exploding an atomic bomb in space.

Christofilos's superiors at Livermore immediately placed his paper under top security control and advised the President's Science Advisory

Committee of its contents. PSAC immediately assembled a panel of twenty physicists to study the paper. In March 1958 the panel issued its report, agreeing with Christofilos's predictions and also urging that a test be undertaken. By late April the Defense Department had decided to carry out one of the largest clandestine operations ever attempted, Project Argus, a series of three atomic explosions in space.

Even as Argus was being planned, the international peace movement was growing in strength and receiving considerable attention. The world was already growing painfully aware of the dose of radioactivity everyone on the planet was receiving as a result of atmospheric nuclear tests. Studies had uncovered radioactive strontium in mother's milk; radiation levels in the New York City area were the highest in the world as result of weather patterns bringing fallout there from test sites in Nevada. Peace activists had trespassed onto the Nevada test sites, and two sailing ships had made their way toward the South Pacific proving grounds in a courageous antinuclear action that captured the world's attention. Recognizing the growing political pressure for a test ban, Eisenhower formally announced that the United States would voluntarily halt nuclear weapons testing upon completion of the current series in October 1958.

Planning for Argus moved rapidly in order to bring it off before the test ban deadline. Early results from experiments aboard Explorer, which had discovered the Van Allen radiation belts, seemed to confirm the first part of Christofilos's theory—that the earth's magnetic field would trap charged particles. In addition to Argus, two very powerful hydrogen bombs were scheduled to be exploded in the atmosphere high above the Pacific. On July 26, Explorer IV was sent aloft with radiation counters to see whether debris from the Pacific blasts would rise into space and be captured by the magnetic field. On August 1, a megaton H-bomb was rocketed forty-eight miles above Johnston Island in the South Pacific and detonated. The blast, according to the Atomic Energy Commission, was "by far the most spectacular shot ever fired by the United States." The fireball rose above the atmosphere, triggering a magnetic storm and blacking out radio transmissions all around the Pacific for several hours from Tokyo to California. The sky was lit for thousands of miles, and Explorer recorded increased levels of radioactivity trapped by the magnetic field in space. Shortly thereafter the second upper-atmosphere test occurred, with similar results. With these tests, another element of Christofilos's theories had been verified.

At launch sites in Virginia, Florida, and Puerto Rico, scientists prepared equipment to fly aboard rockets into the upper atmosphere to measure Argus's effects. The bomb itself would explode above the South Atlantic to take advantage of the fact that the earth's magnetic field dips to its lowest point there, east of the coast of Brazil. In that region, known as the South Atlantic anomaly, it would be easiest to ensure that the bomb exploded at that point within the magnetic field where Christofilos's predicted effects would be observed.

Secrecy was somewhat difficult, due to the fact that the Explorer satellite measuring Argus's radiation belt was part of the International Geophysical Year Program. According to IGY rules, all information gathered by Explorer would have to be made public. However, release of the information wasn't required until after the IGY program was completed, more than a year away. Although Argus was being carried out in total secrecy, its organizers recognized that eventually its results would be known worldwide. No doubt international protest would ensue after it was learned that the United States had tested atomic weapons in the South Atlantic far from its shores and far from its known testing grounds in the South Pacific. However, there would be a year to prepare a justification for the tests.

On the morning of August 27, 1958, the first of three Argus shots was fired. A rocket left the heaving deck of the USS *Norden Sound* carrying a low-yield atomic warhead 200 miles above the earth, where it exploded. Minutes later, nineteen separate rockets were fired into the sky to measure radiation. Near the Grand Canyon in Arizona, a giant metal coil looped across the desert floor measured changes in the earth's magnetism. Observers on board the decks of ships in both the North and South Atlantic stood watch for the auroral displays expected to result from the blast.

As Christofilos had predicted, the glowing and expanding radioactive debris from the bomb blast traveled along the lines of the earth's magnetic field. The action of the material within the field resembled the activity inside the barrel of a recoilless rifle. Half the debris fell immediately into the atmosphere at the site of the blast, producing a wispy, luminescent man-made aurora that lasted for five-and-one-half hours. The other half of the material arched high above the earth and passed across the equator, guided by magnetic field lines to where these lines returned back into the earth's core near the Portuguese Azores. There another aurora, remarkable for its unusual red crown, was observed for an hour and a half. As the bomb debris traveled the magnetic pathway, it released, among other forms of radioactivity, high-energy electrons. The electrons rebounded back and forth above the earth between the blast site and its magnetic conjugate in the north. Parts of the cloud of electrons produced gradually drifted eastward until, within a few hours of the blast, a belt of radiation had encircled the earth. The new belt was later measured from about 200 miles above the earth near the blast site out to 40,000 miles. On August 30 and September 6 the experiment was repeated. The most intense and longest lasting radiation belt was created by the third and last Argus shot.

In the following months, the data gathered from the experiments was analyzed by many scientists concerned with what the Christofilos effects would mean for the design of military space systems. According to the secret report on Argus prepared by presidential science advisor James Killian, nuclear explosions in space produced three types of effects significant to military planning: high-energy radiation effects in space, worldwide radio noise, and intensification of the ionosphere. The extent of each of these effects was determined by the power of the bomb blast, the geographical placement and altitude, and the amount of fission products released. Some of the important effects could be deliberately created and targeted to occur where chosen. There were two important limits to the effects: First, they could be produced over the equatorial and temperate zones but not in the polar regions. Second, although the intensity of the effects increased with the power of the bomb, too great an explosion would cause the earth's magnetism to "burst," so that radiation was not trapped by the lines of magnetic force and no discrete belt formed.

Regions of intensified radiation in space could create havoc with military space systems. In the vacuum of space, there is nothing to dissipate or absorb the radiation. When high-energy electrons strike any object, they generate X-rays. These X-rays are penetrating; they can damage electronic equipment and erase computer memories. They would be lethal to an astronaut. Since the radiation belt would be global and extend outward many thousands of miles, orbiting satellites would frequently pass through regions of intensified radiation. The implication of the test was that near-earth space, the region military planners had been calling the future field of operations, might be an intrinsically vulnerable environment. After the billions had been spent on space stations, space-based missile systems, aerospace planes, and other war-fighting satellites, the entire array of military space equipment might be rendered useless during actual conflict by the relatively simple and inexpensive act of exploding just one moderate-size nuclear warhead within the earth's magnetic field.

Project Argus demonstrated another effect of nuclear explosions in space with potential military consequences. Regions of increased ionization of the upper atmosphere several hundred miles wide were created at both ends of the magnetic field lines crossing the blast point. These regions showed radar reflection and radio absorption. If a nuclear weapon were exploded at the right point above the Indian Ocean, it could wipe out radio communication and reflect warning and guidance radar from Moscow to Leningrad. A blast occurring at the right point over South America could do the same from New York to Chicago.

The increased ionization of the upper atmosphere resulting from nuclear explosions would also prove hazardous to high-altitude bombers and aerospace gliders. A pilot flying above 50,000 feet through a region of intensified ionization would receive a lethal dose of radiation before he or she was able to reach his target. In general, Argus demonstrated that nuclear war would probably disrupt the environment so severely that the usual military preparations would prove of limited effectiveness. Equipment and systems that function well in the normal environment would probably not function in the capacity for which they were designed—to fight a war.

Space warriors may have believed they were merely transferring their military knowledge into space, but war in space in the nuclear age would create conditions for which no strategist could realistically prepare. Defending space systems from nuclear effects might prove impossible. Planning to fight wars in and from space was—and is—an expensive and harmful board-game exercise with little, if any, relevance to a potentially real global conflict.

But the momentum of the space race was already great. Just as the widespread belief that there could be no winners in a nuclear war did not prevent the nuclear arming of the earth, so too, the recognition that space systems would most likely be indefensible and unworkable during a conflict did not slow down the military's moves into space. Its greatest impact was bringing space-systems survivability to the top of the list of military space priorities for the next two and a half decades.

On October 31, 1958, the United States and Soviet Union began a moratorium on the testing of nuclear weapons. For the first time both sides appeared to be serious about reaching a nuclear test ban treaty and arms control. But as the 1960 election drew near, Democratic party politicians became increasingly strident in their predictions of a space and missile gap favoring the Soviet Union. How President Eisenhower handled his own militarists, as well as the negotiations with Khrushchev, would be crucial to the future of the arms race, on earth and in space.

6

The Forming of NASA

Although by 1958 the United States had many ongoing military space projects under the loose control of the Defense Department and DARPA, there was no agency assigned the task of carrying out pure space research or space vehicle engineering unhindered by military considerations. The gathering of preliminary data about the physics of space flight and basic research into the nature of the space environment were largely being neglected in favor of an emphasis on the building of complete, operational military satellite systems. The exploration of outer space, that militarily unessential adventure, had no agency, administration, or organized interest group to carry it out.

In contrast, the Soviets had, since the beginning of their space program, concentrated on dramatic space shots with the goal of manned space exploration. Before 1958 the United States had largely ignored space flight for space flight's sake, instead concentrating attention on space systems for specific military support purposes. America's military satellites required complex new technology and therefore had long lead-time periods from project inception to operations. The Soviets had rockets of greater power (a result of their concentration on large booster rockets in the face of their comparatively primitive sciences of miniaturization and computerization). The Soviets placed simpler requirements on their satellites. Their space program had a centralized, goal-oriented structure, in a regimented society that could be mobilized toward long-term goals.

All of these factors combined to produce an apparent Soviet lead in space that created real political problems for President Eisenhower. He needed to reassure the American people that the United States was not going to be outdone in this new field of endeavor. The White House Committee on Government Organization, under its chairman, Nelson Rockefeller, proposed the creation of a new agency under civilian control that would bring together the scattered U.S. space projects into one organized, national program.

There were, however, a number of obstacles to forming a single national space program. Foremost among them was the military services' reluctance to give up operating in an area they were convinced would soon be militarily crucial. Second, military research is normally carried out behind a shroud of secrecy. But public interest in space activity was already strong and expected to grow. Unless military research was kept outside a single national space program, it would be difficult or impossible to maintain secrecy. Third, if the United States organized its single space program toward military goals it would be greeted by serious adverse international reaction. Space is an international environment. There the only military strategies are, by their nature, global in design; so the development of space vehicles for military purposes would be interpreted as reflecting global imperialist ambitions. Realizing this, the official U.S. space policy declaration noted that worldwide propaganda benefits would accrue to the United States through adoption of the adjective *peaceful* in describing U.S. space activities.[1] However, descriptions adopted for propaganda purposes had little descriptive accuracy.

The organization of America's space program had to maintain peaceful cooperation between the Navy, Air Force, and Army; operate the eight distinct near-term military satellite projects; carry on research on a large number of long-term study projects; catch the Soviets' lead in large booster rockets and space exploration; stir up public support; and maintain the image of an America dedicated to the peaceful, scientific exploration of space. A dual national space program divided into military and civilian sides resulted. According to Dwight Eisenhower's public papers, he "decided that nonmilitary research in outer space could best be conducted by a new civilian agency. But military research would naturally demand secrecy. The highest priority should go to space research with a military application, but for national morale, and to some extent national prestige, this should likewise be pushed through a separate agency."[2]

The National Aeronautics and Space Act of 1958 was introduced into Congress as a result of the president's initiative. Once introduced, the act faced a major challenge from Democratic party space hawks, particularly former Air Force secretary Senator Stuart Symington and presidential hopeful Senator Lyndon Johnson. The Democrats secured changes in the bill that would spell out military prerogatives more clearly. As amended, the NASA act resulted in an apparently civilian agency that was actually subordinate to military authority. The final version of the act states both that "the Congress declares that it is the policy of the United States that activities in space should be devoted to peaceful purposes for the benefit of all mankind" and that "activities peculiar to or primarily associated with the development of weapons systems, military operations, or the defense of the United States shall be the responsibility of and be directed by the Department of Defense." [3]

What would constitute activities peculiar to or primarily associated with military operations? How would NASA and the military services interact? How would the policy that U.S. space activities should be devoted to peaceful purposes for the benefit of all mankind be implemented? These questions became the subjects of heated debates, which have continued into the 1980s.

The National Aeronautics and Space Act created the National Space Council and gave it the responsibility to set U.S. space policy and assure cooperation between NASA and the Defense Department. The council consisted of the president as chairman, the secretaries of Defense and State, the chief administrator of NASA, the chairman of the Atomic Energy Commission, and three additional members appointed by the president.

In forming the new agency, the administration's first task was to gather together various pieces of the space puzzle from the different services. The president requested that the Navy transfer Project Vanguard and the Viking rocket, as well as the satellite tracking network established to monitor U.S. IGY space activities; that the Air Force transfer its research on large-thrust engines and its lunar and interplanetary study projects; and that the Army give up control over the University of California's Jet Propulsion Laboratory and the Army Ballistic Missile Agency's large-rocket program with Von Braun and his over one-hundred-member V-2 rocket team. NASA also absorbed the National Advisory Council on Aviation, including Project Mercury.

The creation of NASA did not occur without some predictable objections from the most vocal space hawks. General Medaris at the Army's Ballistic Missile Agency refused the request to transfer the Von Braun group to NASA. It took a year and eventually a presidential order to bring about the transfer, after which General Medaris retired to write a book critical of U.S. space policy. [4] Both Admiral Hayward, who was in charge of space research for the Navy, and General Schriever at the Air Force unsuccessfully argued that NASA should not be given the authority to contract with industry. They maintained that the power of the purse strings should remain exclusively with the services. But in the end most military spokesmen expressed agreement with the administration's contention that a new civilian agency was needed to carry out the scientific exploration of space, accepting administration assurances that NASA would not interfere with ongoing military projects.

Those in charge of America's military space program recognized some important organizational and budgetary advantages in the new agency. Herbert York, the Defense Department's director of Research and Engineering, explained the Defense Department's reading of the NASA act to a Senate committee. "NASA has the overall exploratory responsibility, and we exploit their results. The Department of Defense's function is to apply the NASA projects to military needs. We can do what amounts to putting a requirement on NASA projects."[5] DARPA's Roy Johnson explained how this would work, by giving the example of moon exploration. A moon base, according to Johnson, was "too far ahead to concern the Department of Defense at this time [1959]. If NASA were not doing the work, the Defense Department would have to, but as it is we can undertake more immediate tasks first."[6] Admiral Hayward put it bluntly: "If I can use their money to get my job done, I will do it."[7] After all, if the Air Force had to explore the moon or the Navy had sole responsibility for upper atmospheric research, then the services' space budgets might well begin to crowd out missiles, bombers, and satellites' military applications.

As long as the military could provide the guiding hand to make certain that NASA didn't stray too far off into militarily useless areas, the military would support the agency. According to General Schriever, the answer to any potential military–civilian conflicts lay in assigning military personnel to NASA and maintaining military power over NASA mission selections.[8] The only major area of potential conflict left in this early military–civilian peace formula came in the area of manned space flight.

By the end of 1959, NASA was in business. Its first semiannual report to Congress showed six different program areas: manned space flight, deep space probes, earth resource satellites, data reception and tracking facilities, launch vehicle development, and the development of nuclear power plants for on-board satellite power. The National Space Council adopted a formal U.S. Space Policy, which directed the U.S. space program "to minimize the psychological advantages which the USSR has acquired as a result of space accomplishments. Select from among those current or projected U.S. space activities of intrinsic military, scientific, or technological value one or more projects which offer promise of obtaining a demonstrably effective advantage over the Soviets, and, so far as is consistent with solid achievement in the over-all space program, stress those projects in present and future programming."[9] The Space Council did not define which areas to stress, but there was no doubt among the general population and the press that "space program" was synonymous with "manned space flight." Despite the decision to stress projects that offered the possibility of overtaking the Soviet lead, there was no way around the fact that the world and the American people were going to stress manned space flight above all other projects. The Soviets, having organized a national space program four years before the establishment of NASA—and in possession of the large boosters required to launch the heavy life-support equipment required by manned space flight—would remain in the lead for several years to come.

It was the astronauts who captured the attention of the public, once they were named and introduced to the American people on April 9, 1959. They became national heroes, prepared to risk their lives in the drive to defeat the feared and hated Soviets in space. With assistance from NASA publicists and Henry Luce's Time/Life empire, which had purchased exclusive rights to the astronauts' stories, the race into space tapped America's seemingly insatiable appetite for competition. Preparation for the space race became the nation's most electrifying entertainment, more popular than any other competition, save perhaps the World Series and the national football championship.

The astronauts' popularity raised a difficult dilemma for the military space planners. General Schriever, for example, may have been pleased by the sudden popularity of the U.S. space program just two years after he was expressly forbidden to use the word *space* in his public speeches. However, the direction the program was going in—toward competition for competition's sake and toward space flight and space stunts as ends in themselves—was troubling. General Schriever simply could not understand the propaganda value of convincing the world public that

American intentions in space were peaceful. "This arbitrary division between space for peaceful purposes and space for national security has an inhibiting influence," he said. "It already has had the effect of holding back military space development." [10]

NASA's Project Mercury space capsule would be basically a converted ICBM nose cone, inside of which an astronaut would be shot into space as high as the rocket would take him before falling back to earth. Shortly after NASA was formed, the Soviets had announced their intention of launching a Sputnik with a man aboard. Mercury, the simplest of the manned space projects, would be ready to launch an American astronaut well ahead of the Air Force's X-20 Dyna-Soar. It was standard military opinion that Mercury would add little to military knowledge, but haste in the competition with the Soviets won out over long-term military significance. Since manned space flight was so terribly expensive and dangerous, Congress and the public would not likely support two overlapping manned space programs. So it was that the very popularity of the NASA astronauts created difficulties for the space militarists.

Americans supported the early NASA space program for many reasons: the sense of national unity it provided, the competition, the feeling of participating in taking the first step on the pathway to the stars, and fear of what the Soviets intended to do high above them. It was not likely that American support would have been nearly as enthusiastic if the nation had pursued the grandiose military space program offered by the Air Force. Nor is it likely that the international community would have accepted that at a time when the nations of the world were fervently hoping to avoid an extension of the arms race into space.

General Schriever testified before Senate hearings on the organization of U.S. space activities in May 1959 and outlined the space systems the Air Force considered necessary. "Space," he said, "is a medium in which many military missions can be performed better than on land, sea, or in the atmosphere. Therefore, it promises to be the arena in which freedom to operate will have decisive military significance in the 1960s and thereafter." [11] Schriever told the senators that the Air Force systems under development, surveillance satellites and ICBMs, were but "forerunners of yet-to-be-developed weapons systems for operations in space." He presented the committee with an Air Force wish list that included manned Dyna-Soars capable of space-to-earth bombardment, an ABM system in space, satellite interceptor and inspection vehicles, advanced communications satellites, meteorological and navigation satellites, mapping and charting satellites, and, to maintain and resupply this space force, a space shuttle. Schriever urged a major national commitment to achieving space weapons capability.

But President Eisenhower, his second term drawing to an end, clearly had his mind set in a different direction. Soviet Premier Khrushchev had come to the United States, and the American president was planning a trip to Moscow. A summit conference between the nuclear powers to discuss a test ban treaty and disarmament was scheduled for Paris. Peace seemed so near that Wall Street suffered a period of peace jitters. The stocks of the major arms suppliers and aerospace corporations fell precipitously.

But on May 1, just one month before the scheduled summit, a U-2 spy plane was shot down over Soviet territory. At first the president, believing that incriminating spy equipment had been destroyed and the pilot killed, denied that the plane had been spying. It had been on a routine weather-monitoring mission from its base in Turkey, he claimed, when it inadvertently wandered over Soviet territory. But when the Soviets produced Francis Powers, the pilot, and his plane intact, Eisenhower admitted the truth. The president tried to salvage the summit by proposing that reconnaissance be internationalized by placing spy planes and satellites in the control of a United Nations agency. Khrushchev rejected the idea and the Paris summit collapsed. A few months later, U.S. spy satellites began routine operations, and the U-2 flights over the Soviet Union were ended.

Eisenhower tried to restrain the rapidly escalating cost of the many missile and space programs, but his last budget was again increased by Congress. He believed NASA should not plan for manned space flights beyond Mercury until the usefulness of space flight could be demonstrated. Among his last gestures as president was the cancellation of NASA's funding for its early work on a manned flight to the moon.

Eisenhower's attempts to control the cost of America's missile and space programs were doomed by the American people's acceptance of deliberately contrived misinformation. Democratic party rhetoric during the 1960 presidential campaign firmly established the missile gap as fact as far as the general public was concerned. Furthermore, there was nearly unanimous belief that the Soviets were ahead in the space race, despite the fact that, by the end of Eisenhower's presidency, sixteen American satellites were circling the earth, as opposed to one Soviet satellite; the United States had sent four spacecraft beyond the moon, the Soviets one.

Eisenhower's frustration with the power of the military-contractor alliance, as evidenced by their lobbyists' ability to undermine his every attempt to bring the space and missile situation under some rational control, came out in his farewell address in January 1961. In his now famous warning, Eisenhower told the American people to guard against "the conjunction of an immense military establishment and a large arms industry," which was "new in American experience" and whose "total influence is felt in every city, every state house, every office of federal government." He urged government to "guard against the acquisition of unwarranted influence, whether sought or unsought, by the military-industrial complex" and cautioned that "public policy could itself become the captive of a scientific-technological elite."[12]

It was left to the next administration to find a way to organize and manage the multifaceted U.S. space program.

7

Manned Space Flight:
The Military and Apollo

When NASA was formed in 1958, the Eisenhower administration assigned it the man-in-space mission in cooperation with the Defense Department, using Air Force ICBM rockets. But General Schriever's Air Force space organization never gave up the idea of having a manned program of its own. At the end of 1960, the Air Force's top missile and space brass—Schriever, General Ritland of the ballistic missile division, and General White, the Air Force chief of staff—organized a public relations and lobbying campaign to influence the incoming administration and win support for an expanded Air Force role in space. An Air Force study report on its future space mission was released to the media. "MORE EMPHASIS ON MANNED SPACECRAFT IS REQUIRED" read the headlines in *U.S. News and World Report*. *Time* liberally spiced its story with quotations from some of the study committee members—General Schriever, Walter Dornberger, and Edward Teller—predicting dire consequences if the nation delayed in developing manned military spacecraft.[1]

Although the Air Force campaign focused on manned space flight, the real issue was to what extent America should militarize outer space, and at what pace. If the United States were to commit itself to asserting active control over near-earth space, then manned vehicles capable of in-orbit maneuverability and interdiction of enemy satellites would be required. If the United States were to commit itself to establishing live command and control over a global battlefield from space, then a manned orbiting space station would be its command center. In order to make military activity in space routine, a reusable manned space shuttle would be the first requirement.

The Air Force study committee recommended antiballistic missiles based in space, a satellite interceptor, and a manned orbiting space station. Clearly the active pursuit of manned military capability would signal a commitment to an aggressive policy in space.[2] Before even a single Russian or American astronaut had left the earth, the debate over a future operational space fleet had begun in earnest.

On the other hand, if U.S. military intentions were limited to the support functions of reconnaissance, early warning, navigation, communications, and meteorology—functions already being provided or on their way in 1960—these would best be accomplished by instrumented rather than manned satellites. The equipment required for an astronaut to survive in space would not only be expensive and complicated, but would take valuable room that could be given over to cameras, sensors, antennae, transmitters, and computers. There was little that an astronaut could do, given 1960 technology, that couldn't be done just as well by sophisticated satellites. Unmanned satellites were cheaper, safer, and more easily kept secret.

The design of manned spacecraft and the design of mission experiments would differ significantly, depending on the spacecraft's purposes, military or civilian. Since the nation could not afford two manned space programs, design and mission decisions made in the early days of manned space flight would determine future directions. As the Kennedy administration prepared to assume office, the Air Force sought to have its new space policy incorporated within the new administration's ambitious goals.

Other interested parties besides the Air Force moved to influence the incoming administration. The House Astronautics and Aeronautics Committee issued a set of recommendations on the future of the U.S. program. The committee criticized the outgoing administration's NASA budget as too meager and listed nuclear rockets and a manned lunar landing as priorities shortchanged by the Eisenhower administration. It recommended that the Air Force be given specific space missions to accomplish but be prevented from organizing a centralized space command, so as not to jeopardize Army and Navy space independence.[3]

Jerome Weisner, whom Kennedy later named his science adviser, prepared the administration's official transition report on space. Weisner's program recommendations were similar to the House staff reports. He agreed that manned space activity should be accelerated, though he fell short of recommending a lunar landing. And he advised that military space activities be increased. However, Weisner believed that control over the military program should be given to the Air Force, so as to decrease project overlap and interservice rivalries.[4]

Before his election to the presidency, John Kennedy had expressed little interest in and even less understanding of the many complicated issues involved in the space effort. Under the NASA act, Kennedy, as president, was to take over as head of the National Space Council. However, Vice-President Lyndon Johnson, who had been involved with missile and space affairs for a decade in the Senate, wanted the job. Johnson had close ties to the Air Force and was a personal friend of fellow Texan Bernard Schriever. His fervent support for space and missile funding had been rewarded with increased economic activity at Air Force bases in Texas. Johnson had also helped prepare and pass the NASA act, and he was publicly committed to the civilian agency's survival. Kennedy, agreeing to a Johnson request, as one of his first acts in office asked Congress to amend the NASA act to allow the vice-president to sit at the head of the Space Council.

James Webb, a close aide to Oklahoma Senator Kerr, was chosen by Johnson and appointed by Kennedy to be the new NASA administrator. Webb, a superb politico, immediately took on the Air Force in defense of his new agency. Webb maintained that, since the NASA act already guaranteed the Defense Department prerogatives, a separate Air Force manned space program would be superfluous. He won support for his position from the new Defense secretary, Robert McNamara, and the new civilian Air Force secretary, Emile Zuckert.

A compromise was reached. Defense Department power over NASA was formalized in a series of organizational arrangements. Webb and McNamara created the Aeronautics and Astronautics Coordinating Board and joint NASA–Defense Department working committees in each area of space activity: a joint committee on launch vehicles, a joint committee on tracking and data relay, a joint committee on manned space flight, and others. Publicly, Webb assured the Pentagon that NASA would fulfill its obligation to provide scientific data and advanced technology developments to the military. Furthermore, he noted that NASA's facilities could easily be transferred to the Air Force at any time the government wished. In a further attempt to pacify the most outspoken space hawks, Webb gave General Schriever's missile and space division an office of Deputy Commander for Manned Space-flight within NASA's organizational structure. Hundreds of other active duty military personnel were also assigned to NASA.

At the same time, the Defense Department moved to consolidate all unmanned military space work in the Air Force. The Air Force Systems Command was established and given overall responsibility for building and launching the nation's space booster rockets, developing equipment and instruments for unmanned satellites, and developing antisatellite weapons. Within weeks of the new administration's coming to office, the many separate space endeavors had been pared down to two: a NASA–Defense Department program under Webb, McNamara, and Harold Brown, the Defense Director of Research and Engineering; and an Air Force program under General Schriever.

On April 12, 1961, three months after Kennedy took office, Soviet cosmonaut Yuri Gagarin became the first man in space, orbiting the earth in Vostok I. NASA was a full year away from being able to accomplish an orbital flight. Alan Shepherd flew the first Mercury into suborbit three weeks after Gagarin's feat.

As with Sputnik, Gagarin's triumph demonstrated Soviet rocket capabilities. Critics of the pace and direction of the U.S. program once again capitalized on Soviet success to argue for more funding. Kennedy, being so new to office, was spared the charges of complacency and failure that had been leveled at Eisenhower, but still he felt the heat. He called Lyndon Johnson in and asked him, "Do we have a chance of beating the Soviets by putting a laboratory in space, or by a trip to around the moon, or by a rocket to go to the moon and back with a man? Is there any space program which promises dramatic results in which we could win?"[5] One thing was clear: If the United States were to overtake the Soviets in the accomplishment of dramatic space spectaculars, then the space program would have to be organized around a single goal—one that was exciting enough to win the support of the people, far enough in the future to allow time to catch up with Soviet rocket technology, yet near enough to be within sight.

Johnson held a series of discussions on establishing goals for the nation's space program. He met with Webb and his assistant, Hugh Dryden; Wernher von Braun; General Schriever; Admiral Hayward; Jerome Weisner; and the other members of the National Space Council: George Brown of the Brown & Root Construction company; Donald Cook, American Electric Power Service; Frank Stanton, Columbia Broadcasting System (CBS). Out of these meetings a consensus was reached that America should aim to land a man on the moon before 1970. Official goals for the national space program were established. They included: the earliest practicable achievement of manned lunar exploration; early worldwide operational satellite communications capability; early worldwide weather prediction capability; aggressive scientific investigation of outer space; and a large booster rocket program capable of meeting both civilian and military needs.[6]

On May 25, 1961, President Kennedy told the American people, "Now it is time to take longer strides—time for a great new American enterprise—time for this nation to take a clearly leading role in space achievement, which in many ways holds the key to our future on Earth. I believe that this nation should commit itself to achieving the goal, before this decade is out, of landing a man on the moon and returning him safely to earth."[7] With these words, the new president set the tone and style of the U.S. space program in the 1960s. America was to get to the moon, and get there first. From that point on, when people thought of space, they would think of the moon as the place they were headed. Now NASA flight would be seen as a step on the trail to the lunar surface. If the Soviets accomplished a particular space achievement first, rather than arouse a flurry of criticism and fear, it would spur a new commitment to accomplish the ultimate goal.

The moon goal was undoubtedly successful in motivating the American people for a time. However, it also further distorted the American economy in the direction of large-scale capital-intensive military or semimilitary endeavors, occasioning huge federal budgets while leaving the main questions unanswered: What would we do on the way to the moon, and what would we do when we got there?

With the Apollo moon landing established as the nation's space goal, the Air Force presented its space program to the Defense Department for approval. The Air Force proposed keeping their manned space flight program alive through work on and use of the X-20 Dyna-Soar, which was then being studied as a weapons system under the name Dyna-MOWS (Manned Orbiting Weapons System). The Air Force requested a funding increase for Dyna-Soar. At the center of the new program was a proposed space station, MOL (Manned Orbiting Laboratory), to be used in combination with a space shuttle to ferry men and equipment into orbit. When the Air Force presented its space proposals in a report to Secretary of Defense McNamara and Defense Director of Research and Engineering Harold Brown, the paper was promptly returned to General Schriever, as outlandish and provocative. That began a five-year feud between Schriever and the McNamara Defense Department.

McNamara's approach to military space activity was to build slowly and deliberately from the set of military satellites that were just becoming operational. The first military satellites had been launched in 1958; by 1962 over fifty had been orbited. By the time the Kennedy administration took office, the Air Force's Discoverer reconnaissance satellites were operational. The Satellite Missile Observation System, SAMOS, had recently begun successfully transmitting video information to ground receivers. The Navy's Transit satellite system for radio navigation of submarines and missile-carrying aircraft was being tested, so too the Army's communications relay network. The Air Force's electronic "ferreting" satellites were scheduled to begin locating and recording Soviet radar and radio transmissions within a year. And the Air Force had an attempt underway to demonstrate long-range communication through radio backscatter off a band of orbiting tiny copper filaments, in hopes of providing a system to maintain communication in the event of the ionospheric disruptions expected to occur in a nuclear war. Project West Ford, as this scheme was known, was eventually proven unworkable after at least one launching of billions of tiny copper filaments.

For every satellite circling the earth there were second- and third-generation improvements under development. These unmanned satellites offered considerable military opportunities, which were only just beginning to be exploited. McNamara and Brown wanted emphasis placed on unmanned satellites since the military advantages of manned spacecraft were still uncertain. They'd leave it to NASA to demonstrate the spaceworthiness of manned spacecraft. But General Schriever repeatedly pointed out that, if the Air Force was one day going to rely on manned vehicles, their design requirements would be significantly different than what NASA would require for its missions. A military spacecraft would need the ability to take off with little preparation and land at militarily secure sites. On the other hand, NASA would have time to plan ahead for launch dates and could afford to depend on militarily ludicrous landings in the middle of the ocean. Maneuverability, re-usability, and controlled reentry capability, all technologically formidable requirements, were considered crucial by General Schriever but unessential for NASA's mission to the moon. Schriever lobbied hard for the Air Force's experimental manned space vehicle, the X-20 Dyna-Soar. He argued that, although the moon goal was important, it shouldn't crowd out the funding for a manned military spacecraft. But McNamara pointed to the extremely high cost of manned space flight and refused to place a high priority on the Dyna-Soar until the Air Force could prove its military value. Schriever, in turn, argued that the Air Force would never prove the Dyna-Soar's utility if it never got a chance to fly. But to McNamara, the United States was already far ahead of the Soviet Union in space technology of proven military value. He hoped to further enhance American superiority by steadily improving and expanding the nation's satellite network. Expensive and unproven manned space vehicles might dissipate America's limited resources. So, although the Air Force's Dyna-Soar continued as a research project, Dyna-MOWS, it failed to receive the level of funding it needed to reach the launch pad.

By the end of 1961, the United States had been flying military satellites for three years. The Soviets had still not launched a satellite for a specific military purpose. In the spring of 1962, before the United Nations, the Soviet Union proposed an agreement banning all military activity in space. But shortly thereafter, the Soviets launched their first photoreconnaissance satellite, indicating they'd entered the military satellite race.

With NASA's astronauts and the Soviet's cosmonauts receiving all the public attention, the military space program retreated farther behind a wall of secrecy. The Defense Department set a policy prohibiting prior announcement of U.S. military space launches. In addition, the code names of the satellite projects—Discoverer, SAMOS, etc.—names that had routinely been added to the aerospace vocabulary, were all classified. Henceforth, the mere mention of a project's name would be a breach of government security.

8

Further Nuclear Tests in Space: The Rainbow Bombs

There were enough military satellites orbiting and working by 1961 to say that a coordinated system had become operational. The satellites formed an important link in a global electronic network being created to improve fighting capability around the world. But the global wars being planned for in 1961 would probably involve nuclear weapons. And even as this network was being set in place, there were disquieting suggestions that it might not work in an actual nuclear war. The results of the series of nuclear weapons tests that had ended in 1958, particularly the test explosions in the upper atmosphere and in space, had revealed unexpected side effects that could incapacitate electronic equipment and black out radio communications.

The military faced a complicated and expensive dilemma, one that has haunted planners in every administration since. Every improvement in nuclear warfare technology led to further reliance on advanced electronic equipment, exactly the kind of equipment most vulnerable to the side effects of nuclear explosions. The only way to be certain that equipment would work when required would be to test it under battle conditions, including during and after nuclear explosions. But both sides had suspended nuclear testing in 1958. It would have been politically untenable for the United States to resume nuclear tests while test ban negotiations with the Soviets proceeded. Yet a sizable chunk of the national wealth since 1958 had gone into the largest military buildup in the history of the world. Much of it was dependent on equipment and systems no one could be certain would function under the conditions of nuclear war for which they were made.

President Eisenhower's efforts to reach a test ban agreement with the Soviets had been undermined all around him. Atomic Energy Commission Chairman John McCone lobbied extensively against the test moratorium and against any test ban treaty. As he wrote in his diary, he was "maneuvering public opinion, including the Senate, so that the President will have a very difficult time getting a treaty ratified." [1] Among others campaigning against a test ban or moratorium were the members of the study committee on the Air Force's future in space: Bernard Schriever, Edward Teller, and Walter Dornberger.

The atomic weapons tests in space, Project Argus, had revealed facts about the behavior of radiation and radioactive debris that were significant for the design of future military spacecraft. Pressure had been placed on President Eisenhower almost immediately after the conclusion of Argus, in 1958, to repeat the tests with bombs of greater power, farther out in space. Eisenhower's Defense secretary wrote a memorandum to the president urging that nuclear tests in space be resumed to obtain information on the "effects of nuclear explosions in a hitherto relatively unexplored environment which may be of vital importance to our future defensive posture." [2] The Defense Department and the Atomic Energy Commission drew up plans for a series of tests, including further tests in space, in the event of the resumption of testing.

The pressures to resume nuclear weapons testing grew stronger as Kennedy began his term of office. Test ban negotiations were going nowhere. They were stuck in old patterns of Soviet-American distrust. The Soviets felt that the Americans wanted to ban testing in order to maintain current U.S. superiority. The Soviets tried to couple a test ban with nuclear disarmament. To the Americans, Soviet insistence on complete nuclear disarmament was an attempt to accomplish at the negotiating table what they could not accomplish in the field—a reversal of U.S. superiority. To Moscow, America's insistence on "verifiability," acceptance of mutual means of assuring compliance with the treaty, was an attempt to legitimize U.S. spy-in-the-sky activity and so further improve U.S. targeting capabilities. To Washington, Soviet refusal to agree to inspection or overflight was a way of maintaining the advantage of secrecy they held with their police state.

Complicating the test ban debate were the suspicions on both sides that the other was contemplating the placement of nuclear weapons aboard orbiting satellites. Weapons tests in the upper atmosphere in 1958 pointed to the havoc that might result from the detonation of high-yield nuclear bombs above enemy territory. The yield of the 1958 bombs was just over one megaton—about fifty times more powerful than the Hiroshima bomb. Some of the bombs being fashioned in 1961 had yields of up to fifty megatons. A system of hundreds of multi-megaton orbiting bombs would mean that one would always be in a position to reenter the atmosphere on command from earth. If a single such bomb exploded over a nation's heartland, vast territories might be incinerated. With the institution of orbiting nuclear weapons, a global sword of Damocles would be hanging overhead. There is evidence from Soviet literature that high military authorities lobbied for the development of such a system as a shortcut to balancing the strategic equation then heavily weighted in America's favor. The United States had a similar system under study as Project NABS (Nuclear Armed Bombardment Satellites). Since both sides appeared capable soon of orbiting nuclear weapons, both sides also stepped up their antisatellite efforts as a defense against such weapons.

Tension dominated the international atmosphere in the spring and summer of 1961, challenging the new administration at the same time as the first dramatic steps were being taken in manned space flight. On the stage of international affairs and power balances, space accomplishment and military strength interacted in complex and contradictory ways. On April 12, 1961, Soviet cosmonaut Yuri Gagarin became the first man to orbit the earth. Nikita Khrushchev, as was his pattern, attempted to use Gagarin's success to highlight Soviet rocket power, and by implication ICBM capabilities. But by this time American reconnaissance satellites had revealed Khrushchev's missile boasts to be bluffs. The Soviet ICBM "force" stood, at most, at fourteen missiles, none loaded with weapons and all so heavy they needed to be transported to their launch site by rail, making them highly vulnerable to an American counterforce strike. The Soviets had no bombers on alert, no overseas bases near America's shores, and no operational military satellites. A missile gap existed, but it wasn't the same one the Democrats had parlayed into a term in the White House. Worse yet, from Khrushchev's standpoint, the Americans knew about the imbalance. He feared that the new president might be emboldened to make his international moves without regard to Soviet power. In the new situation created by satellite reconnaissance, the Soviets could no longer use secrecy to keep the Americans wary.

In comparison to the Soviet Union, the United States was bristling with the arms of intercontinental warfare. As a result of the missile and

satellite developments begun in the 1950s and accelerated by the fic-
titious missile gap, the United States had constructed four separate
missile fleets all aimed at targets in the Soviet Union. The United States
had forty Atlas ICBMs targeted at the USSR from within America's
borders. Additional Thor and Titan intermediate-range missiles were
stationed at forward bases in Turkey, Italy, and Great Britain. Polaris
missile-firing submarines capable of striking deep within Soviet territory
without warning were frequently within firing distance. Over six hundred B-52s were stationed at Strategic Air Command bases, some few
always loaded, in the air, and ready to strike. In addition, more than a
thousand B-47 long-range bombers were combat-ready. To assist this
arsenal, space technology in reconnaissance and navigation satellites
had advanced to the point where satellites were about to make targeting
over intercontinental distances precise enough for weapons to be fired
directly at Soviet home forces, eliminating in a first strike any threat of
retaliation.

But as unequal as the balance of power may have appeared, balance-
of-power equations were no longer simple in the age of weapons of mass
destruction. No amount of American power could guarantee that not a
single Soviet bomb would retaliate. Even if only one bomb made it to
one city, millions of casualties would result. The Soviets, sitting on the
weaker side of the power equation, understood it to be in their interests
to emphasize the equalizing factor introduced into balance-of-power
calculations by the enormity of nuclear destruction.

The real measure of international power, as the Soviets saw it, was
the ability to win the hearts and minds of the masses of people living in
the newly independent nations that had emerged during the postwar
decline of colonialism. In this competition, the Soviets' dramatic space
accomplishments would be used to demonstrate, according to
Khrushchev, the superiority of the socialist system. The Soviets also
vowed to expand their influence in the Third World by supporting
nationalist and pro-Communist elements in their fight against Western
economic and political control.

In the competition for the loyalties of the Third World the United
States suffered a number of defeats, none more dramatic than Cuba.
First, Cuba's new revolutionary leaders were courting the Soviets.
Then, when the United States organized an invasion by CIA-trained
Cuban exiles at the Bay of Pigs, it failed due to poor planning, faulty

equipment, and an underestimation of Castro's popular support. In the aftermath, American officials lied about U.S. involvement. Confronted by the evidence, President Kennedy publicly took responsibility for the invasion and its failure. Privately, he worried about American credibility in the wake of the fiasco. The Bay of Pigs invasion occurred just five days after Yuri Gagarin's spectacular orbital flight aboard Vostok I. The juxtaposition of America's humiliation in Cuba and the Soviets' triumph in space not only upset Kennedy, but the American people as well. It was within this context that the president requested Lyndon Johnson to undertake a reevaluation of America's space efforts, which led to the decision to organize NASA's program around a lunar landing.

With both sides anxious about the limits of their power, the stage was set for a clash of wills, which occurred first over Berlin and then over Soviet missiles in Cuba. The situation in Berlin had been stalemated since the crisis of November 1958. To the Soviets' dismay, West German military power continued to grow. So too did the West's attraction to large numbers of East Germans, particularly to technicians and other skilled laborers. In addition, West Berlin was becoming a growing propaganda nuisance far behind the lines of the Eastern bloc. The Soviets continued to threaten to sign a peace treaty with the German Democratic Republic (GDR), giving the East Germans power over access to Berlin and canceling Western right of passage. At a meeting between Kennedy and Khrushchev held just weeks after the Bay of Pigs, Khrushchev reiterated his intention to eliminate Western power in Berlin. In response, Kennedy vowed to defend Western access to the city. He called up the reserves and announced increases in American military strength. On August 13, 1961, in a surprise move, the Soviets constructed the Berlin Wall. One problem, the flight of East Berliners to the West, was brutally resolved.

Concern was growing throughout the world that the superpowers, who had failed to reach a test ban agreement, were about to turn international tensions into another round of global contamination by weapons-test fallout. President Kennedy, feeling the heat from his military advisers, warned the Soviets that the United States would not forego testing nuclear weapons indefinitely. Two weeks after the appearance of the Berlin Wall, Khrushchev announced that the Soviet Union was about to renew atmospheric nuclear tests. The first such test occurred the following day. The three-year-old test moratorium had ended.

Leaders of northern European nations, those likely to receive the brunt of the fallout, quickly protested. The popular African leader Kwame Nkrumah traveled to Moscow to ask Khrushchev to halt the tests. The Soviet leader told him the tests were necessary to shock the West into negotiations over disarmament and Berlin. Apparently, Soviet leaders believed that only a dramatic demonstration of the unworldly power of nuclear weapons could prevent the Americans from using the threat of its nuclear superiority to gain leverage in Berlin. The Soviets announced their intention to test 20- to 100-megaton bombs, the most powerful weapons yet exploded.

President Kennedy responded with a decision to begin underground testing, hoping to avoid an all-out renewal of atmospheric tests. On September 10, the Soviets exploded a multimegaton bomb in the Arctic. In October, bombs of thirty and fifty-eight megatons were exploded. When Soviet cosmonaut Marshal Titov orbited the earth aboard Vostok II, Khrushchev boasted, "If you want to threaten us from a position of strength, you do not have 50- and 100-megaton bombs. We have stronger than 100 megatons. We placed Gagarin and Titov in space, and we can replace them with other loads that can be directed to any place on earth."[3] Such talk did not make Americans sleep easily.

Soviet weapons tests were carried out in the upper atmosphere where, by intensifying the ionosphere and generating electromagnetic pulses over a large area, the effects on the electronics of communications and radar were greatest. American scientists had little information about how nuclear explosions affected sophisticated electronics. For this reason, among others, the president decided to renew aboveground nuclear testing. In March 1962, he explained his decision, saying, "We are spending great sums of money on radar to alert our defenses and to develop possible antimissile systems, on the communications which enable our command and control centers to direct a response, on hardening our missiles and their warheads from defensive action, and providing them with electronic guidance to find their targets. But we cannot be certain how much of this preparation will turn out to be useless; blacked out, paralyzed or destroyed by the complex effects of nuclear explosions."[4]

The Atomic Energy Commission presented its plans to the administration for a new series of tests that would include two H-bomb explosions in space. The first, code-named Starfish, would be a 1.4 megaton bomb, over a thousand times more powerful than the Argus explosions, to be detonated at 250 miles altitude—just beneath the Van Allen Belt region. Following this blast would be a multimegaton bomb at 1200 miles altitude, well within the radiation belt. The two tests, along with others planned for the upper atmosphere, formed a high-altitude test series to be known by the code name Project Fishbowl. Project Fishbowl was but part of Project Dominic, a larger series of tests of a number of devices at many altitudes and on the ground. Dominic was scheduled to begin in April in the South Pacific.

Many scientists questioned whether a megaton blast in the Van Allen regions wouldn't "burst" the Earth's magnetic field. Too large a nuclear explosion could expel bomb debris through a temporary crack in the field, perhaps causing the Van Allen Belt to empty its contents into the atmosphere and out into deep space, in effect eliminating it until it built up again through newly captured solar and cosmic radiation. Some scientists thought the belt would re-form in a matter of days; others predicted it would take a century. Nobody could be certain of the effects of Van Allen Belt disruption on the planetary ecology. Similar uncertainties in 1958 had led scientists to keep the explosive power of the Argus bombs low—around one kiloton. However, by the time the Fishbowl experiments were being planned, with the nation moving rapidly toward the routine use of space for military purposes, scientists wanted to observe the effects of much larger explosions farther out in space than Argus. After the president announced plans to carry out the new test series, the popular press began speaking of "rainbow bombs," in reference to the dramatic auroral effects they were expected to produce in widely disparate regions of the globe.

As the public awaited the rainbow bombs, scientists around the world organized in protest. The most outspoken and influential was the eminent British astronomer Sir Bernard Lovell, who called the tests "an affront to the civilized world [and] one of the most dangerous experiments ever devised. . . . The Americans," continued Sir Bernard, "are taking unilateral action against the accumulated wisdom and advice of those who still have freedom to speak in the international community with an utter contempt for the grave moral issues involved."[5] The Committee on Space Research of the International Council of Scientific Unions, the organization that had sponsored the International Geophysical Year, protested the American plans. A statement signed by eleven leading American scientists, including two former presidents of the American Association for the Advancement of Science and a Nobel laureate in medicine affirmed, "The Earth's environment is not the domain for potentially disruptive experimentation. No individual and no nation has the right to tamper with the vast balance of nature."[6]

Government scientists defending the tests pointed out that on the scale of the cosmos in which they were working, the proposed nuclear explosions would amount to mere fireworks. Lovell responded directly to that defense with the observation that the earth, too, is minute on the cosmic scale and hanging in a delicate balance by natural forces. He further commented, "The proposals to make nuclear explosions in space arise from a small group of military scientists, unknown and unidentified to the world at large, who have persuaded their masters to make a series of huge gambles under the guise of defensive necessity."[7]

The world's diplomats, already discouraged by the resumption of testing on both sides, were equally disturbed over the rainbow bombs. The United Nations had only recently formed the Committee on the Peaceful Uses of Outer Space, to which both the United States and the Soviet Union belonged. Any progress the committee might hope to make toward reversing the trend toward further militarization of space would be severely compromised by the U.S. plans to test nuclear weapons there.

As June approached, and with it the scheduled date for the rainbow bomb explosions, members of the Woman's International League for Peace and Freedom stood vigil outside the White House, asking that the space tests be canceled. At a news conference the president was asked whether the proposed tests would jeopardize the official U.S. policy to restrict outer space for peaceful purposes. "No, I don't think so. I don't think so," Kennedy responded. He failed to answer the question about U.S. policy, instead speaking to the concerns expressed in the press about the Van Allen Belt: "I know there's been a disturbance about the Van Allen Belt, but Van Allen says its not going to affect the belt, and it's his."[8]

On June 4 the first launch of a bomb in the Fishbowl series was attempted. The electronic systems failed and the Thor rocket, with its nuclear payload, was deliberately destroyed two minutes prior to explosion. Fragments of the bomb fell into the Pacific Ocean south of Johnston Island. The following day U.N. Secretary General U Thant called the Fishbowl tests "a manifestation of a very dangerous psychosis which is in evidence today."[9] Two weeks later the Johnston Island South Pacific launch site was again ready for launch. This time the tracking system failed and again, moments after launch, the mission was aborted. Fragments of the unexploded bomb, with its highly radioactive warhead, sank to the bottom of the ocean.

Finally, on the third attempt to explode the first of the rainbow bombs, on July 9, 1962, Starfish burst into space. Crowds had gathered on beaches all over the South Pacific, as they had every night of a scheduled attempt. At eleven P.M. in Hawaii, they saw it. The stars were washed out by a bright pink light that gradually deepened and darkened until the sky was tomato red, blood red. Daggers of yellow and green light broke through the clouds. The crowd on the beach gasped, cheered, and shuddered. They at least knew to expect dramatic visual effects. In Samoa, two thousand miles from the blast, terrified natives fled from their villages in the bush toward the coasts as the sky above them lit up with a nightmare of colors for fifteen minutes. A reporter in Pago-Pago, Samoa, heard one fleeing man shout, "Crazy white man!"

This explosion was not yet the main event. Starfish exploded at an altitude of 250 miles over the South Pacific, below the lower fringes of the natural radiation belt, with a force of 1.4 megatons. The blast was too strong to be contained by the magnetic field, as Argus had been, and a shower of radioactive debris went spaceward, intensifying the Van Allen Belt. The intensified belt reached as low as 200 miles altitude, with a peak of intensity at 800 miles. There radiation levels were one hundred times more intense than the normal peak levels of the belt. Seven operating satellites were eventually crippled by the radiation in the belt, including two secret Air Force satellites and the joint British-American research satellite, the Ariel. Some of the satellites were destroyed immediately as a result of the shower of high-energy electrons that struck their shells and exposed sensors. Others decayed over time as they repeatedly passed through zones of intense radiation. As the press leaked the news that the Starfish effects had been more severe than government scientists had originally predicted, concern over the next rainbow bomb increased. The next one was to be placed well within the Van Allen Belt and deliver a larger punch.

Due to the early launch failures, the test series was running behind schedule. President Kennedy had earlier promised that the series would be completed by the end of August. Worldwide protests, particularly in Great Britain and America, were growing stronger by the day and becoming a real political threat. Although the United States never formally canceled the final rainbow bomb, the last high-altitude explosion took place in September 1962, only thirty miles high.

As far as we know, the Starfish explosion on July 9 was the last nuclear weapon to be detonated in space. With the completion of testing in both the United States and the Soviet Union, the superpowers were once again talking about a test ban treaty, and negotiations reopened. By the following summer the Treaty Banning Nuclear Weapons Tests in the Atmosphere, in Outer Space and Under Water was signed.

9

The Early Sixties:
Cold War and Peace

Nineteen sixty-two was a year when space and cold war were on everyone's mind. In February, John Glenn rode a NASA Mercury capsule to become the first American to orbit the earth. In March, the *New York Times* reported that the Air Force was developing the new laser light technology for use in future antisatellite weapons. In May, Scott Carpenter became the second American to orbit when his Mercury craft circled the earth three times.

In June, the Air Force reasserted its manned space program by announcing plans to go ahead with the development of a manned satellite interceptor vehicle capable of maneuvering and rendezvousing with satellites or spaceships in orbit. In July, the Starfish rainbow bomb was exploded, demonstrating to military space planners just how little anyone understood about the complicated effects of nuclear explosions in space. In August, Vostok III and Vostok IV were launched within twenty-four hours of each other into orbits that would bring the two spaceships and their cosmonauts within eyesight of each other in the first in-space demonstration of rendezvous techniques.

In September, tensions between the Soviet Union and the United States reached a historical peak during the Cuban missile crisis as the Soviets brazenly attempted to assemble their own forward bases in the Caribbean. Khrushchev underestimated the length to which the Americans would go to prevent such a move, and for a few days the world lived near the brink of nuclear holocaust.

In October, Senators Barry Goldwater, Howard Cannon, and Thomas Dodd publicly charged the Kennedy administration with holding back the military space program. In December, the Defense Department canceled Air Force plans for its satellite interceptor, Project SAINT.

Throughout the year the rift between Air Force space hawks and the

McNamara Defense Department grew wider. Robert McNamara attempted to bring cost accountability to defense procurements. The United States should consolidate and improve its current military superiority, McNamara believed, rather than embark on another round of buying new, expensive, high-tech weapons. Numerous missile and satellite systems were just being put into operation, four years after their construction had begun in the post-Sputnik flurry of military activities. For every weapons system under way, there were ten proposals for something better, more precise, more deadly. As McNamara explained, "Our problems of choice among alternatives in weapons and weapons systems have been complicated enormously by the bewildering array of entirely workable alternative courses which our technology can support." [1] Facing an embarrassment of technological riches, McNamara tried to assert what he called "quantitative common sense."

McNamara's quantitative common sense often took the form of obscure cost-benefit equations figured out by the economists he had brought into the Defense Department. But according to the Air Force and other military space supporters, there was no way to quantify or predict what benefits the United States might someday garner from a position of military superiority in space. They believed that a manned military space program ought to continue, despite the costs, in order to find out what military astronauts could accomplish. The Air Force finally crystallized its space goals after years of internal debate. For the mid to late sixties, the Air Force would focus on three main areas: satellite rendezvous and inspection techniques; a manned orbiting space station to ascertain the feasibility of manned reconnaissance, communications relay, and the potential of space stations as command centers in future global wars; and advanced communication satellite systems in geostationary and polar orbits.

President Kennedy found himself in the middle of a feud he was ill prepared to settle. Only one year after the National Space Council had established the lunar landing goal for NASA's Project Apollo and assigned the military space missions to the Air Force Systems Command, the compromises these decisions represented had begun to unravel under the pressures created by the aggravated Cold War and Defense Department fiscal constraints. Despite sharp rises in space expenditures in each of the first two years of the new administration, pressure mounted to expand space activities even more. Supporters of the Air

Force space mission pointed to continued Soviet successes in launching heavy vehicles and demonstrating in-orbit maneuverability as reasons to expand the Air Force's program to include manned spacecraft. In particular, they wanted an experimental manned space station and maneuverable space vehicles for satellite rendezvous and inspection. In July 1962, the president asked that all the parties involved in the nation's space efforts prepare an especially critical review of the work being done.

In response, Secretary McNamara reported to the president that he believed NASA's progress in manned space flight was satisfactory, the military program had begun to pay off in strategic benefits, and there were "no valid new requirements which justify at this time a major expansion in the military space program."[2] According to the secretary, a clear distinction should be made between manned and unmanned military space activities. He believed that the Air Force's unmanned programs should continue at high levels of priority and expenditure but that NASA, in close cooperation with the Defense Department, rather than the Air Force should continue to run the nation's manned space program.

Air Force Secretary Eugene Zuckert, who one year earlier had helped NASA ward off General Schriever's move to capture the manned space flight assignment for the Air Force Systems Command, broke with Secretary McNamara. He reported to Kennedy, "Space technology is reaching the point, I believe, where specific military and psychological warfare possibilities are emerging. Future operational requirements also appear to warrant a definite program leading to a manned orbital space station. That program will provide a base of trained experienced manpower and facilities for development of military capabilities."[3]

Space flight is an extremely expensive affair. All parties agreed that it would be difficult for the nation to manage two separate and distinct manned space programs. NASA's costs were already rising above estimates and voices were heard in Congress questioning the money being spent in space. There were also widespread doubts remaining about whether a manned military presence in space, and the arms race that would probably accompany such a presence, would improve American security in any way. To McNamara, compromise could be achieved by making certain that all major civilian space programs be integrated with military requirements in the early stages of their development. On the surface McNamara's position was an ideal compromise. However, difficulties were bound to arise in trying to reconcile the military's insistence that NASA integrate military requirements into the civilian program with NASA's mandate to achieve the lunar landing ahead of the Soviets, within the decade, while still controlling costs. Military requirements would complicate an already demanding task.

By 1962 the military potential of the moon had been largely discounted. General Boushey's moon-base studies had dropped to a low level of priority. The military was mainly interested in near-earth space and geosynchronous orbits. Therefore, Project Apollo's military value was far from clear. But NASA had an interim project—Gemini—that would test the techniques of orbital flight with a two-person spacecraft. Gemini spacecraft would fly in low-earth orbit and test the in-space maneuverability and rendezvous techniques that Apollo would require. Gemini was the obvious place for a NASA–Air Force compromise. The first Gemini flights would not occur until 1964 or early 1965, leaving plenty of time to integrate military requirements into the project. With McNamara's Defense Department set against a separate manned military space program, military participation in Gemini became the Air Force's best hope for keeping its long-term space goals alive. With Gemini perfecting rendezvous techniques the Air Force's manned satellite interceptor project, SAINT, would become unnecessary. Air Force experiments in manned reconnaissance, remote sensing, and space medicine, intended for the space station, could be performed aboard Gemini instead. If the Air Force should later receive its own space station, the experience acquired through Gemini could be used to develop an earth-to-space shuttle.

Although for a while the Air Force held out for its own Gemini capsules and its own Gemini program (which the Air Force dubbed Gemini Blue), the issue was resolved by an agreement between NASA and the Defense Department establishing the Gemini Planning Board, which made Gemini a joint military-civilian project. As a result, in December, Air Force Project SAINT was officially canceled by the Defense Department after six years of research. The X-20, Dyna-Soar, was threatened with a similar fate. But the Air Force Systems Command managed to convince the Defense Department that, since Gemini was designed without a controlled reentry capability, continued development of the Dyna-Soar aerospace glider was necessary. However, Dyna-Soar funding remained below what it needed to proceed to a foreseeable launch date.

The Gemini Planning Board was established to make the major decisions regarding the missions and experiments to be flown aboard Gemini flights. Although the board was to be divided equally between members representing the Defense Department (military) and NASA (civilian), it turned out to favor the military. Both NASA and the Defense Department were to have three representatives. The Defense Department appointed Undersecretary of the Air Force Brockway McMillan, Deputy Director Albert Hall, and General Schriever from the Air Force Systems Command. Representing NASA were NASA Associate Administrator Robert Seamans, who had been chief designer of Air Force reconnaissance satellites for RCA; Admiral Boone, on assignment to NASA from the Navy as NASA's deputy administrator for Defense Affairs; and George Mueller, a deputy NASA administrator. Two out of three of the NASA members had a strong military orientation. The establishment of the Gemini Planning Board became, in effect, a takeover of NASA's manned space flight mission by the military in exchange for the Air Force delaying its own manned program.

But despite the militarization of NASA's Gemini program and despite the fact that President Kennedy had nearly doubled the 1963 military space budget over the previous year's allocations in response to the dual orbiting flights of Vostoks III and IV, the space hawks remained angry over McNamara's reluctance to grant the Air Force an independent, top-priority manned space program. Senator Goldwater complained that McNamara's "whiz kids," by which he meant the economists in the Defense Department, were getting in the way of the Air Force space program.

President Kennedy was particularly upset over an article in *Readers' Digest* in August 1963 by the *Digest*'s military editor, Francis Drake, who claimed that the administration was neglecting the need for an expanded military presence in space. The article, entitled "We're Running the Wrong Race with the Soviets," featured a long quotation taken from Walter Dornberger's address before the Air Force War College. Dornberger, vice-president of Bell Aeronautics and former head of the Rocket Division in Hitler's Army, claimed that when the Soviets were ready they would

. . . bring war into space and from space back to earth. We must be aware that they have a head start. They have reliable high-thrust boosters, accurate navigation and guidance systems. Today they place payloads in space five times heavier than ours. In a few years they will be able to rendezvous in space, a crucial point in military operations. Having resolved this decisive problem, there should be no major difficulty anymore in establishing a man-operated military system. They won't rest until they have obtained complete control of the space effort. They may achieve superiority in a couple of years, while we are still arguing about the usefulness of military space systems. [4]

Dornberger's claim that the United States was failing to develop a military space capability disturbed Kennedy. He asked Vice-President Johnson, as chairman of the National Space Council, whether Dornberger's charges were true. Johnson reassured the president that the Gemini program would develop rendezvous technique, control and guidance capabilities, and improvements in propulsion—all of which had military significance and could be drawn on by future military spaceplane designers.

NASA administrator Webb personally responded to the *Reader's Digest* article in a confidential memo to the president in which he estimated that "75-80% of the cost of the Apollo program will be devoted to the development of a capability for conducting near-earth orbital operations which could form the basis for any military systems we may require." [5] Kennedy apparently accepted Johnson and Webb's assurances. In any event, he was already trying to head off competition in space through tentative steps toward cooperation with the Soviets.

The first formal offer of cooperation came from Soviet Premier Khrushchev in a letter to President Kennedy in February 1962, congratulating John Glenn and the American people for the success of America's first earth-orbiting space flight. The president, after conferring with his aides, had replied to Khrushchev's vague offer with a list of specific suggestions for cooperation in global weather monitoring, mapping of the earth's magnetic field, satellite communications, and the sharing of space medicine information. The Soviet premier accepted Kennedy's proposal, and the president asked NASA's deputy director, Hugh Dryden, to open talks with his Soviet counterpart on establishing a program of cooperation. [6]

This hopeful first step failed to bring the space powers together. It occurred at the peak of cold war tensions. A summer of nuclear weapons tests and the Cuban missile crisis intervened. However, one channel of communication remained open for the antagonists to discuss space issues: the newly formed United Nations Committee on the Peaceful Uses of Outer Space, in which they both participated.

Space talks in the United Nations were stuck in the same pattern that characterized disarmament negotiations. The Soviets insisted on all-encompassing declaratory bans, which were unacceptable to the Americans because they relied on mutual trust rather than verification procedures. The Americans proposed specific, verifiable agreements that tended to avoid broad commitments and formalize U.S. positions of superiority. Between these positions there existed a large gap but little actual room for maneuvering toward compromise. In the spring of 1962, the Soviet Union proposed a ban on all military activities in space, including satellite reconnaissance. The Soviets, in a move directed against U.S. plans to encourage private industry to enter the field of commercial satellite communications, also insisted that the U.N. adopt a principle forbidding activities by private enterprise in outer space.

Through the cold war summer of 1962, there was as little progress in the U.N. as elsewhere. But by early in 1963, the Soviets had softened their position. They dropped their insistence that all military activity in space be banned; they had begun a spy satellite program of their own. They also dropped their objections to private communication satellites. The first U.S.-Soviet space cooperation pact was signed. Both parties agreed to joint launchings of weather-monitoring satellites and cooperation in testing communications satellites. In addition, the Soviets proposed an agreement specifically aimed at preventing either side from establishing an orbital nuclear bombardment system. The proposed U.N. treaty would ban the placement into orbit of "any objects carrying nuclear weapons or any weapons of mass destruction."

According to Ray Garthoff, an official in the State Department at the time, President Kennedy conferred with representatives of the various national security agencies concerning the Soviet proposal.[7] The Defense Department, the National Reconnaissance Office, the CIA, and the Joint Chiefs of Staff all opposed declaring a ban on nuclear weapons in space. The Joint Chiefs argued that the United States should keep all its space options open. They opposed any agreement to ban or limit weapons in space because they believed such an agreement would require international inspection of military launch sites for verification and they opposed such inspection. At the same time they argued that no agreements should be signed that lacked means of verifying Soviet compliance. Knowing that the Soviets were bound to object, the JCS suggested to Kennedy that he offer the Soviets an American counterproposal calling for stringent verification procedures. The Soviet objections to inspection would then effectively mask American objections on the same score. The focus of the debate would be shifted away from space weapons and to verification. But since a nuclear weapon could be made to fit inside a suitcase, hiding one within a satellite would be simple and virtually impossible to detect; insisting on it would be simply a means of avoiding a treaty.

Kennedy believed that a joint declaration banning nuclear weapons in space was in the national security interest of both nations. He questioned the Joint Chiefs' stratagem of always demanding verifiability without regard to the particular issue under negotiation and instructed America's U.N. ambassador to work for a declaratory ban. It came in the form of U.N. resolution rather than a treaty. According to Garthoff, a treaty would have been possible, but Kennedy, expecting objections from right-wing space militarists and their congressional supporters, opted for a resolution rather than a treaty, which would have required Senate approval.

By the spring of 1963, momentum was building toward peaceful cooperation. In Europe and the United States, antinuclear weapons activists were making political gains through their strong moral stands and powerful acts of civil disobedience. Although the world had survived the Cuban missile crisis the previous fall, for a few days the tenuous nature of survival in the nuclear age had been apparent to nearly everyone. In addition, more and more information on the health effects of radioactive fallout was becoming available. Circumstances combined to create an international demand for an end to nuclear weapons tests in the atmosphere. In August, the superpowers signed a test ban treaty. If Soviet-American cooperation on earth and in space was ever to be possible, now was the time to begin.

The summer of 1963 also marked a peak of activity in the early civil rights movement. Throughout America there was a growing belief that the fight against poverty and racism at home was at least as important as fighting communism abroad. Within this new political context the more blatantly competitive aspects of the Soviet-American space race began to appear absurd and frivolous.

The arguments in favor of cooperation in space were clear and compelling. Most of the uses to which space technology would be put—weather forecasting, international communications, ocean navigation, and remote surveillance of earth resources—were global in nature. Efficiency would demand global cooperation. In the other major area of civilian space activity, the scientific exploration of the moon and planets, competition resulted in the two space-faring nations spending what to most people was unimaginable wealth on duplicating each other's efforts and concealing the results. Many people were asking why, on the cosmic scale, did it matter whether the first people to walk on the moon were Marxists or capitalists? Why shouldn't space voyagers be planetary ambassadors? But as long as earthbound military ambitions fueled each nation's rockets, cooperation would be preempted by competition and distrust. Likewise, as long as competition and distrust dominated Soviet-American relations, military ambitions in space would predominate over space exploration and the development of space technology for peaceful purposes. The key to the demilitarization of space lay in improved Soviet-American relations. The first step toward cooperation on earth might well be agreeing to the demilitarization of space.

Perhaps as a result of seeing how close the world had come to the brink of destruction over the Cuban missile crisis the year before, perhaps for personal reasons, President Kennedy began to seek areas of potential cooperation with the Soviet Union. A healing process in relations between the two nations had begun. In June 1963, a U.S.-Soviet communications link, "the hotline," was established. In August, the test ban treaty was signed. The same month, in a speech at American University in Washington, President Kennedy made a dramatic appeal to the Soviets to seek a relaxation of tensions. Three months later, at the U.N. General Assembly, Soviet Foreign Minister Andrei Gromyko spoke of his nation's desire to cooperate with any and all nations in space. Kennedy followed Gromyko at the United Nations with a speech on September 23. In a surprising gesture that perhaps could have dramatically changed Soviet-American relations—and with them the future of space exploration and development—President Kennedy invited the Soviet Union to participate with the United States in landing astronauts on the moon. He told the General Assembly,

> Space offers no problem of sovereignty. By resolution of this assembly, the members of the United Nations have foresworn any claims to territorial rights in outer space and declared that international law and the U.N. Charter will apply. Why therefore should man's first flight to the moon be a matter of national competition? Why should the United States and the USSR, in preparing for such expeditions, become involved in immense duplications of research, construction, and expenditure? Surely we should explore whether the scientists and astronauts of our two countries, indeed of all the world, cannot work together in the conquest of space, sending someday in this decade to the moon, not a representative of a single nation but the representatives of all nations. [8]

The president had discussed the contents of his speech with almost no one before its delivery. He had inserted the invitation just prior to addressing the General Assembly. Those most involved with the nation's space program, hearing press accounts of what sounded like a decisive shift in U.S. policy, were surprised. Many were dismayed. Some press commentators saw Kennedy's speech as a way of slyly extricating himself from the commitment to a projected lunar landing, which was likely to be far more costly than originally estimated. Apollo was already under attack from the Left as a waste of resources better spent on social programs, and from the Right as a drain on resources that could be better spent to build a military space force. For the first time since the inception of NASA, Congress had reduced the space agency's budget below what the president had requested, by $400 million. In addition, the noted British astronomer Sir Bernard Lovell had returned from a tour of the Soviet Union and reported that the Soviets had abandoned their manned lunar efforts and were concentrating instead on sending unmanned payloads to the moon's surface to carry out scientific experimentation. Further, Lovell had stated his belief that the Soviets were sincerely interested in space cooperation.

Although it is possible that in light of increasing demands on the nation's treasury and the possible absence of Soviet competition, Kennedy feared a movement of popular support away from NASA's manned lunar mission, he likely meant what he said—an international program of space exploration would make better economic and political sense and might help bring about peaceful coexistence on earth. Two months before his speech, in answer to a reporter's query about the possibility of a joint Soviet-U.S. mission to the moon, Kennedy had dismissed the idea as impractical because it would "require a breaking down of a good many barriers of suspicion and mistrust and hostility."[9] With his speech at the United Nations, he had taken a major step in breaking down those barriers.

But the president failed to build support in Congress, NASA, the military, or the general public for such a dramatic change of direction. The response in Congress to Kennedy's gesture was quick and hostile. Olin Teagues, chairman of the House Subcommittee on Manned Spaceflight, told reporters, "We have backed the program because we believe it is vital to our national security,"[10] implying that if the administration was suddenly inviting the Soviets to participate, then either the program was not vital to national security and therefore need not be supported, or national security was about to be compromised by the administration in the name of Soviet-American cooperation. In response, the House first cut further funds from NASA's Apollo budget request and then passed an amendment to the NASA authorization bill, prohibiting NASA from spending any of its money for participating in a manned lunar landing to be carried out jointly by the United States and any Communist, Communist-controlled, or Communist-dominated country, thereby undermining Kennedy's U.N. speech. The Senate later weakened the budget amendment so that it only prohibited any joint space programs without prior congressional consent, but the message was clear: There was little likelihood of winning consent for a joint lunar landing.

President Kennedy was assassinated in November 1963. Had he lived and fought for his space cooperation proposal, history might have been very different. President Johnson publicly claimed that he supported Kennedy's move and promised to pursue areas of cooperation with the Soviets. But Johnson had a long history of ties to military space interests. It was unlikely he would act without their approval, as Kennedy apparently had. Little more was heard about Soviet-American space cooperation for the next decade.

10

The Air Force–Defense
Department Feud

President Kennedy's sudden proposal for an international lunar landing, followed by Congress's subsequent obstruction of the offer, demonstrated a chronic problem American leaders had in trying to organize U.S. activities in space: The United States did not have a clearly defined policy. There was a propaganda line—that "activities in space be devoted to peaceful purposes for the benefit of all mankind"—but as yet no major space activities were being thus devoted. Decisions about the course of U.S. space activity were made by compromise between two conflicting military space strategies: one formulated by the Air Force Systems Command, dominated by General Schriever and his political supporters; the other by Defense Secretary McNamara and Research Director Harold Brown. Lyndon Johnson, as chairman of the National Space Council during the Kennedy presidency, played a major role in working out the compromises that had led to the Gemini decisions. As president, his position between the two sides remained unchanged. The two sides themselves, despite the Gemini compromises, grew farther apart as their positions hardened.

By 1964, the Air Force space agenda had crystallized around three main areas: manned spaceplanes, space weaponry, and global command and control systems in space. Air Force plans were based on the simplistic belief that battles in space would be fought with the Soviet enemy much as air battles had been fought during World War II. After all, the Air Force had been born in that war; its leaders and heroes were made in dramatic air battles. They foresaw space dogfights with shrapnel or laser light exploding around brave space pilots in satellite interceptors, skillfully dodging enemy fire at 20,000 miles per hour; aerospace glide bombers courageously fighting their way to enemy targets at lightning speed; space command centers where astronaut generals brilliantly moved strategic assets across an extraterrestrial battle space: These were the visions that motivated spacehawk generals.

The problems with these Air Force fantasies were legion. First, they routinely failed to take into account the astounding costs and long development times required to deploy all the elements of their imagined aerospace force. Second, they failed to consider how the rest of humanity living on this globe might feel about a U.S. aerospace force expropriating the space around them for American military ambitions. Third, they underestimated the difficulties of the environment itself—the harshness of it and how vulnerable space pilots would be in an arena where there would be no bailing out. Fourth, they disregarded evidence suggesting that the effects of nuclear explosions would close near-earth space to manned military operations and possibly render all electronic systems there inoperable. And fifth, they did not have the political support required to make a long-term commitment to fielding a military force in space. No political context existed except in extreme right-wing circles, to even argue for a space force, since most Americans believed their government's contentions that it was primarily interested in peaceful scientific exploration.

The opposing agenda put forward by the McNamara Defense Department was both more reasonable and more sophisticated than Schriever's but no less directed toward military purposes. The most significant difference was that the Defense Department's space plans were based on America's nuclear weapons strategy, whereas the Air Force seemed to believe they would leave nuclear weapons behind when they traveled into space. The Defense Department believed that the military space systems of prime necessity were those designed to enhance America's nuclear capabilities and refine nuclear strategy. Therefore, emphasis should be placed on unmanned satellite systems for improved reconnaissance, targeting, warning, guidance, and communications for global military forces, rather than on developing forces for fighting in space itself. Top priority, according to Harold Brown, should go to research on achieving satellite survivability in the event of nuclear war. Once Defense planners were assured that space systems could be protected under what Brown termed "all conditions of systems nullification," then they might proceed to the kind of ambitious arsenal proposed by the Air Force.

The Defense Department was not opposed to the militarization of space; they merely disagreed with Air Force brass as to the scope and pace of military activities feasible there. The Defense Department believed that military capabilities should be developed by a building-block approach: begin with unmanned satellites, move up to reusable spacecraft to make access to space less expensive and more routine; and perhaps later, after NASA had developed the necessary space flight capabilities, move toward a manned space force in the twenty-first century.

The Air Force Systems Command under General Schriever disapproved of the building-block approach, favoring proceeding with research vehicles in the tradition of the Air Force's X series of airplanes. According to Schriever, the only way to learn how an aerospace glider would fly would be to build an X spaceplane, as the Air Force was doing with the X-20 Dyna-Soar, and allow it to be tested to the limit of its capabilities. The only way to test Air Force astronauts' ability to carry out useful military activities for extended periods would be to place them in an Air Force space station and see what they could do.

But these extrapolations into space of what were familiar Air Force research procedures in developing aircraft ignored the fact that space was fundamentally different than the atmosphere. The costs of research spacecraft would be far greater than research aircraft. The Defense Department believed that NASA space vehicles should be used as they were intended, as research vehicles in developing space flight technique for the military. However, as General Schriever pointed out, the requirements for military vehicles would be significantly different than those for scientific exploration. But neither the Air Force nor the Defense Department was politically prepared to go before the American people and the world and admit that the real purpose of America's space activities was to develop military capabilities. Consequently, the American people continued to believe they were paying for a scientific program of space exploration with the immediate goal of landing a man on the moon. They did not realize that the major decisions regarding that program were being made as compromises between two conflicting military perspectives, each agreeing that the space agenda the public was looking at—peaceful scientific exploration of space—was largely a luxury tolerable only as long as the nation felt rich enough and excited enough by its results to continue to pay for it. It is no surprise that the U.S. space program appeared to lack direction, since so many of its decisions were taken as choices between two hidden agendas.

The second group of NASA's manned space flights, Project Gemini, was scheduled to begin early in 1965. The compromise that had been reached between the Air Force, Defense Department, and NASA in late 1962 guaranteed that Air Force experiments, thirteen in all, would be carried out aboard Gemini and that General Schriever would have an active role in determining Gemini missions. This compromise dealt with only one aspect of Air Force–Defense Department disagreements; manned satellite interception. Gemini would maneuver toward and rendezvous with a target object, a refitted Air Force Agena upper-stage rocket. With Gemini developing rendezvous techniques, the Air Force canceled its SAINT (Satellite Interceptor) program. But the Air Force did not accept that Gemini could replace other projects, particularly the X-20 Dyna-Soar and a manned orbiting space station. Furthermore, the Gemini compromise dealt primarily with manned space flight and left unresolved the issue of space weapons.

As Lyndon Johnson began his presidency, major decisions regarding the long-term future of the United States in space had to be made. Johnson had to decide between two conflicting visions of America's military future in space and whether the United States was going to have any civilian program at all after the Apollo missions were completed. Because of the long periods of time needed to plan, design, and build complicated space vehicles, work on any new program would have to be started in the mid-sixties. Johnson's choices were complicated by the growing U.S. military involvement in Vietnam and by the fact that public support for NASA was slipping. Polls showed that a majority of Americans in 1964 believed money could better be spent elsewhere. Johnson's options were complicated even more by a presidential election campaign that had Republican candidate Barry Goldwater claiming that Kennedy's Apollo decision had permitted the Soviet Union to increase its lead in the competition for control of near-earth space.

Rather than preparing a clearly articulated national space policy with definite goals and steps to achieve them, Johnson carried on as Eisenhower and Kennedy had before him. He dealt with each individual project as it came up. One of his first acts after becoming president was to give preliminary approval to the Air Force's manned orbiting space station. At virtually the same time, Defense Secretary McNamara announced that the X-20 Dyna-Soar project was being reviewed to see if it unnecessarily duplicated work being done under Project Gemini. On

December 10, 1963, the Defense Department officially canceled the Dyna-Soar. McNamara explained that the expected billion-dollar price tag was simply too high for the limited objectives the research vehicle would achieve.

The cancellation of Dyna-Soar was a severe blow to General Schriever's strategy. To his mind, a vehicle streamlined enough to be rocketed to orbital speeds of just over 15,000 miles per hour and able to reenter the atmosphere in a controlled glide to land on an Air Force runway was essential for building a manned space force.

Some kind of winged aerospace glider had been under consideration since Dornberger had brought his plan from Germany to Bell Aviation. In 1960, Boeing Aircraft had been chosen to build a Dyna-Soar prototype for suborbital tests. By 1961, the Air Force was looking at Dyna-Soar's potential as a reconnaissance vehicle, a high-speed bomber, and as a space shuttle. By the summer of 1963, just a few months before McNamara canceled the program, a schedule had been set for initial orbital flights to begin early in 1966.

McNamara's Defense Department pointed out that the Gemini spacecraft, while not as controllable as Dyna-Soar was projected to be, did have sufficient lift to correct its reentry trajectory and would thus provide some experience in pilot control. Furthermore, the technologies and materials required for controlled reentry could be researched using unmanned vehicles. Air Force Project START (Spacecraft Technology and Advanced Reentry Techniques) was begun to continue the relevant aspects of Dyna-Soar while canceling the main vehicle program.

With the cancellation of SAINT and Dyna-Soar, the Air Force manned space program was whittled down to planning a manned orbiting space station with an Air Force spacecraft to serve as a shuttle to the station. Next, McNamara's Defense Department canceled further studies on one of the space hawks' most ambitious unmanned weapon schemes, Project BAMBI (Ballistic Missile Boost Interceptor). The studies for an antiballistic missile (ABM) system based in space had been funded by the Advanced Research Projects Agency and the Air Force Systems Command since 1959. BAMBI would have involved hundreds of armed satellites, each one equipped with small heat-seeking self-guided missiles that could, theoretically, be launched down to earth to strike Soviet missiles as they were rising from their launch pads. Missiles only just rising out of their silos would be relatively easy targets compared to those same missiles minutes later descending onto their victims at meteoric velocities.

The space ABM system would not only have involved the orbiting of hundreds of missile platforms; it would also have required defensive weapons in space to protect it from counterattack. It would additionally require periodic visits from a shuttle with engineers on board to maintain and repair the system. Furthermore, the guidance technology for BAMBI would have involved aiming over hundreds of miles within an accuracy of a few feet at a moving target from an orbiting platform traveling over 23,000 feet per second. Even if BAMBI's technological hurdles could be overcome, the number of countermeasures available to an enemy would be nearly infinite. The satellite launchers themselves could be attacked. Thousands of missile decoys could be launched to exhaust the space ABMs' capacity. The sensitive devices required for guidance would be vulnerable to all forms of jamming and overdosing. A truly viable space ABM system, with its complex technologies for guidance, command, control, repair and maintenance, and defense, would be more expensive than all the missiles and bombs on earth combined. The Defense Department believed BAMBI extremely premature and politically provocative. If pursued, such a system would lead to an arms race in space that was in no one's interest. (Fifteen years later the space ABM project would be resurrected and adopted by the Reagan administration. See chapter 16.)

The Defense Department objected to orbiting weapons systems not only on technological, economic, and military grounds, but also for international political considerations. The Space Age may have been opened by Soviet and American rocket power, but it was kept open by an international consensus that rejected any claims to state sovereignty in space and guaranteed freedom of overflight passage to peaceful earth-orbiting satellites. The principle of open skies in space was established when the early Sputniks and Explorers circled overhead and no nation objected. When the United States orbited its first spy satellites in 1959, the Soviets complained but raised no serious challenge to their free passage. Four years later the Soviets began launching their own spy satellites. However, armed satellites passing over friends and enemies alike could easily shatter the international consensus recognizing freedom of passage.

The Defense Department recognized that freedom to operate in space was uniquely important to the United States. The Soviet Union bordered the regions of potential future Soviet-American conflict: Europe, Asia, and the Middle East. Presumably the Soviets placed less importance on the development of satellite systems for intercontinental military support. The United States was far ahead of the Soviets in the uses of space for communications, guidance, and surveillance. The Soviets, given their central geographical position, could maintain forces near the potential trouble spots while relying on conventional means of command and control. However, America was on the opposite side of the globe from regions it considered strategically essential. Satellites could help maintain centralized command over forces stationed in and around distant strategic lands and thereby offset the advantages the Soviets enjoyed by virtue of their central geographical position. Freedom of space was essential to the building and maintaining of an intercontinental command and control network. According to Defense strategy, the United States had far more to gain by preserving the principle of no state sovereignty in space than it did by deploying armed satellites. Since freedom to operate in space was more strategically valuable to the United States than to the Soviet Union, it would presumably be more in the Soviets' interest to deploy orbiting weapons to threaten that freedom. Certainly it made no sense for America to be the first to introduce weapons into orbit and thereby give the Soviets an invitation to do likewise. Such an act would jeopardize the security of both nations, to the greater detriment of the United States.

The United States did not have to forswear the capability of destroying enemy satellites; that could be done just as well by shooting at them from earth. An orbiting satellite travels along a highly predictable path. If you know where it is, you can easily launch a bomb to explode near it. Blast effects in space, not being attenuated by the atmosphere, have very large destructive ranges. You don't even need to be very close to your target. The United States had already tested antisatellite weapons (ASATs) that had been launched from the ground, from the decks of ships at sea, and from beneath a high-flying jet fighter. The means to fire missiles from satellites would not add significantly to the U.S. ASAT arsenal and would, in the bargain, threaten the principle of open skies in space. The Air Force desire for ASATs, BAMBI, and bombs had more to do with the space hawks' shoot-out fantasies than with any actual military and political condition. McNamara rejected all Air Force schemes for orbiting weapons.

Nineteen sixty-four was an election year, and presidential candidate

Barry Goldwater attacked Johnson for his Defense Department's cancellations of SAINT, Dyna-Soar, and BAMBI. The Republicans promised that if elected they would redirect the nation's space program toward control of near-earth space. Johnson defended his record against Republican charges that he had been soft on the Russian threat from space. During the campaign he announced the deployment of two antisatellite systems—one Air Force and one Army—both using ground-launched missiles based in the South Pacific. These were the first missiles known to be aimed at targets in space. They had been deployed for a year before Johnson made them public for obvious political reasons during the campaign.

Shortly after winning the election, Johnson ordered NASA to reevaluate its long-range priorities and begin looking beyond Apollo to the future of the civilian space program. The moon landing was only three or four years in the future. Planning and development of a post-Apollo manned space flight program could take many years. If a smooth transition to a new goal was to be accomplished, work would have to begin soon.

NASA established the Future Programs Task Group. The group prepared its report for the president and outlined the difficult dilemma facing NASA in the mid-sixties. The need to begin post-Apollo planning was obvious: NASA's budget, however, was already overcommitted to current projects—Gemini, Apollo, Surveyor lunar probes, and Mariner's missions to Venus and Mars. The report concluded that unless NASA's budget was increased significantly, a very unlikely prospect, top priority had to go to programs already under way. Design and feasibility studies for future programs would have to be delayed.

Indeed, there was little chance of NASA's budget being increased. The space agency was dependent on popular support, and that support had begun to slip. The congressional act that had created the agency also stipulated that its budget come up for yearly congressional review. By 1965, NASA's funding began to appear to Congress as one of the most expendable of the government's budget demands. The federal budget was rising steeply in response to the costs of President Johnson's Great Society domestic programs and the accelerating war in Vietnam. Interest in NASA began to lag as the war and the domestic turmoil of the sixties grabbed center stage in the nation's consciousness. More and more people perceived NASA's activities as a luxury the nation could no longer afford. The result was that NASA was too financially and politically insecure to plan for the 1970s and 1980s. Even as Project Gemini began its first highly successful missions, Congress was cutting NASA's funding.

Each successive Gemini mission demonstrated further space flight capabilities. For the first time since the beginning of manned space flight, American astronauts performed space spectaculars in advance of the Soviets—Gemini IV, the first space walk; Gemini VI and VII, a rendezvous within ten feet of each other; and the final Gemini flight, a successful docking totally controlled by the pilot. Thirteen Air Force experiments were carried aboard the Gemini flights, six of them on the joint Air Force NASA mission Gemini V. The military involvement in Gemini received extensive international press coverage and raised concerns over military activity in space. Most Americans still believed that the Gemini flights were warm-up exercises to the main event—the moon landing. Since the United States still had no publicly articulated or even secretly formulated policy or strategy concerning the eventual military uses of manned vehicles in near-earth space, the purpose of the Gemini experiments was unclear. The administration and the Defense Department still did not have a clear idea of what tasks military astronauts might eventually perform.

This uncertainty was exactly General Schriever's arguing point. He urged that final approval be given to the Air Force's space station, Project MOL (Manned Orbiting Laboratory), in order to determine the feasibility of using a space station as command post for military operations on earth and as a reconnaissance vantage point from which astronauts could control cameras and monitor enemy radio and radar transmissions. MOL would consist of a forty-two-foot cylindrical station and a modified Gemini capsule to ferry the astronauts to the station and back. Once MOL was approved, the next step would be a reusable, controlled reentry shuttle that could begin to open MOL and its command-post descendants to routine and economical usage. Shortly after Gemini V, on August 25, 1965, President Johnson officially announced his approval for full development of the Air Force MOL, with initial launch dates set for 1968. After years of trying, General Schriever and the Air Force Systems Command was finally granted its own manned space program. President Johnson named General Schriever to head Project MOL.

As the Gemini program got under way and America appeared to overtake the Soviets on the way to the moon, partisans of the numerous aspects of the U.S. space program geared up for the competition to determine America's future in space. The Senate held hearings on the subject, the President's Science Advisory Committee (PSAC) issued a report, the National Academy of Sciences (NAS) Space Science Board held a study conference, and the Air Force and Defense Department prepared their plans. A civilian-military split was becoming apparent. The civilian scientific community stressed the development of planetary exploration capabilities. The military focused its attention on near-earth space.

Both the National Academy of Sciences and the PSAC post-Apollo panel expressed concern that the post-Apollo program would be dominated by the military. According to the PSAC panel, unless a vigorous planetary exploration program was initiated, with the ultimate goal of exploring the planets with manned spacecraft, America's space program would be focused on near-earth space, where the military had majority interest. NASA's planetary science program had already marked some exciting successes with unmanned probes to Mars and Venus, and civilian scientists were beginning to plan for dramatic probes in the 1970s. The National Academy of Sciences recommended a vigorous space sciences program leading to a manned landing on Mars and "manned earth orbital programs for rescue, service of unmanned vehicles, and several military objectives, such as inspection, but these should be a secondary, not a primary, goal."[1]

The Air Force and the Defense Department had no particular quarrel with planetary exploration, but clearly both believed America's space priority should be the utilization of near-earth space for military purposes. With the MOL program under way, a brief period of calm reigned between McNamara and Schriever. Schriever's major concern, after getting MOL into orbit, was development of a reusable controlled reentry shuttle vehicle. Defense Department goals were becoming ever more down-to-earth. America's involvement in a land war in Vietnam put pressure on Defense research organizations to work on systems for combat. In 1965, Harold Brown, McNamara's director of research and engineering, testified before the Senate post-Apollo hearings and described a satellite system the Defense Department was working on that would coordinate targeting between land units and their support bombers and transmit signals to artillery units and troop transporters to provide them an exact three-dimensional fix on their location. As for major post-Apollo achievements, Brown gave top priority to the "ultimate achievement of hardened components and circuitry design which offer high resistance to radiation," and second priority to "reusable spacecraft." [2] Both the Defense Department and the Air Force encouraged NASA to develop reusable controlled reentry vehicles, the kind of spacecraft Defense had dropped with its cancellation of the X-20 Dyna-Soar. NASA responded by establishing a study group to review the total national program on developing reentry vehicles.

No major decisions came out of these post-Apollo debates. By 1966, Vietnam had become a full-scale war, and the nation was embroiled in its accompanying distress. Military spending climbed to 45 percent of the federal budget over the next three years. With money for Medicare, Social Security, veterans' benefits, and interest on the national debt all committed by law and therefore beyond congressional control, NASA appeared as the one big-money item open to major cuts. Over the three-year period 1966–68, NASA's budget was cut by over a billion dollars, further eroding its ability to plan ahead.

The brief peace between Schriever and McNamara broke down over issues of money and war. Pentagon research and development budgets, including funding for MOL, were squeezed by the needs of the ongoing war. Harold Brown, Schriever's nemesis for five years, was appointed Air Force secretary. Furthermore, Schriever took exception to President Johnson's handling of the war, joining right-wing critics who were upset that the Air Force wasn't being allowed to "bomb them into the Stone Age," as Curtis LeMay put it. Moreover, Schriever was particularly upset over the delay in getting on with work on a maneuverable reentry spacecraft, which he thought both he and Defense had set as a priority. According to Schriever, by 1966 he had "had enough of McNamara. Every time we'd talk about a major new technology development, McNamara would worry that it would lead to a weapons need and cost money. I didn't like the policy with regards to the Vietnam war, I didn't like the policy with regards to major weapons systems and technology. We were at cross purposes at everything." [3] Schriever retired from the Air Force Systems Command and Project MOL. As retired generals tend to do, he set up his own consulting firm and went to work for the aerospace industry as a free-lance consultant on major weapons systems development. He soon joined with Edward Teller and Trevor Gardner, his former colleagues on the 1961 Air Force study committee on the Air Force in space, as early supporters of Richard Nixon's presidential bid.

Increasingly, the American Right criticized both McNamara's de-

fense policies and Johnson's science advisers' recommendation for expanded planetary exploration. Barry Goldwater preserved his role as the
space hawks' spokesman in the Senate. Goldwater lashed out at
McNamara for indicating

> . . . that space weapons are too costly, as though any dollar
> amount is too high for the security of 190 million Americans and
> a billion allies and friends. The only major space-military pro-
> gram McNamara has permitted to stay alive is the MOL. We
> have deployed one or two so-called satellite killers, but they are a
> pitiful particle of what is really needed. Pictures of Mars are fine.
> So is a trip to the moon. But the first job of any administration is
> to secure the nation against its enemies. We will not remain the
> most powerful nation on Earth for long if we don't reverse the
> suicidal Johnson-McNamara refusal to let us arm ourselves in
> space.[4]

Even Phyllis Schlafly, who later earned her fame as an antifeminist
activist, joined the space militarists' cause. With retired Admiral Chester Ward, she wrote the book *Strike from Space*, in which she claimed
that the Soviets were perfecting a doomsday weapon to be dropped onto
America's heartland from space. She even claimed that the war in
Vietnam had been deliberately instigated by the Soviets in order to
divert America's attention away from the space arms race. As for Apollo, Schlafly argued that "the U.S. moon program need not be canceled—just postponed until we can afford a $30 billion non-military
luxury. Wouldn't you rather spend those billions on space interceptors
and orbital bombers to assure the safety of your home and family?"[5]
Goldwater and Schlafly's sentiments were echoed by Walter Dornberger, who used his retirement from Bell Aeronautics to dismiss the
moon landing as a "stunt" lacking in military virtue and to urge that in
the post-Apollo period major emphasis be given to a space shuttle
transportation system. "The next time we must create an environment
in space that will be used by men, not only for research but for military
purposes. For this we require a logistics system, a recoverable, reusable
space transporter to carry people and supplies back and forth to space."[6]
As the Apollo landing approached, a consensus had begun to develop
among the space hawks for a space shuttle in the post-Apollo period to
open near-earth space to routine military uses. Among space scientists,

a very different consensus was being reached to pursue planetary explo-ration. As the Johnson administration descended into the quagmire of Vietnam, it was obvious that decisions about America's future in space would have to await the end of the war or the end of the administration.

NASA had few defenders left. The Right attacked it for its nonmili-tary stunts; liberals attacked it for stealing resources from social services. Neither criticism demonstrated an understanding of the propaganda function NASA served for the nation's military–aerospace industry co-alition. The manned space programs of the United States and the USSR were still, ten years after Sputnik, the means to distract attention away from the global military ambitions each nation's rockets and satel-lites were intended to serve. But by the mid to late 1960s, America's Right didn't want a propaganda front to conceal their military aims— they were proud of them. And America's Left, angered by being reg-ularly lied to about the war, no longer trusted official propaganda at all.

The situation was further clouded when NASA was enlisted into the war effort by the Defense Department to determine how certain space technologies might be applied to the fighting. One such study, Project Able, was a resurrection of the old German space war concept of using orbiting mirrors to direct beams of sunlight toward enemies on earth. Project Able was a somewhat more modest concept for using sunlight reflectors to illuminate the jungle battlefield at night. Though the sun-light reflectors never made it into orbit, the Defense Department did begin to exploit satellites for direct combat tasks for the first time in the history of space flight. Satellites were reported being used to direct the bombing of North Vietnam.[7]

At the same time the United States Senate was considering ratifica-tion of the Outer Space Treaty, which had been finalized in the United Nations in December 1966. The treaty asserted that space is "not sub-ject to national appropriation by claim of sovereignty, by means of use or occupation" and charged the signatories not to "place in orbit around the earth any objects carrying nuclear weapons or any other kinds of weapons of mass destruction." By signing the treaty, the United States agreed that "exploration and use of outer space, including the moon and celestial bodies, be carried out for the benefit and in the interest of all countries."

There was rarely any attempt to reconcile U.S. proclamations about the "peaceful uses of outer space for the benefit of all mankind" with actual ongoing military activity. One of NASA's original purposes; in fact, was to showcase peaceful U.S. space activities in such a way that the military could go about its business unimpeded by the constraints of international posturing. That NASA's propaganda functions might be undermined by its reduced role in the post-Apollo period was one of the Presidential Science Advisory Committee's major concerns in recommending a post-Apollo planetary exploration program. "The predominantly civilian character of the overall U.S. space program is more appropriate to the international posture which the United States traditionally wishes to present than would be a scaled-down effort in which the military might be the dominant part."[8]

By 1967, with the world's attention on Vietnam and the moon race, the military was already the dominant part of the American space program. That year, the Department of Defense launched 61 objects into space, compared to 21 by NASA. And the United States was by far the dominant nation in space. By the beginning of 1967, out of the 209 satellites to orbit the earth since the beginning of the Space Age, 162 were American, 41 Russian, and there were 2 each for the French, British, and Canadians.

Although by the time of Apollo U.S. military interests clearly dominated the space program, most of the public's attention was turned to the final leg of the moon race. In 1967 tragedy struck the space programs of both the United States and the Soviet Union, postponing the lunar finale for a year. On January 27, a fire broke out as astronauts Grissom, Chaffee, and White were carrying out inspection and practice of their Apollo spacecraft when a faulty wire sparked. In the pure O_2 atmosphere in the cabin, the spark quickly became a conflagration, killing the crew of what was to be the first manned Apollo flight. Subsequent investigations implied that the Apollo program was being hurried beyond the point of safety in order to achieve victory in a competition most Americans already perceived as childish and dangerous. North American Aviation, Apollo's prime contractor, was judged responsible for shoddy work. In the late-sixties atmosphere of budget cuts and public cynicism, the catastrophe appeared to threaten NASA's entire future. Three months later, Soviet cosmonaut Komarov was killed during a reentry accident in the first Soyuz spacecraft, delaying future Soviet manned space flight as well. The following year, the moon race resumed, but with a new twist: the United States appeared to be in it alone.

11

The Moon Landing and
Its Aftermath

Lyndon Johnson had been involved in the politics of space and missiles for twenty years. More than any other politician, his career was associated with America's voyage into space. It was fitting that the Apollo 10 astronauts should circle the moon and return to earth on Christmas week 1968, only a month before Johnson's political career would come to an end. The Soviets, meanwhile, dropped their efforts toward a manned lunar landing and announced they were concentrating instead on unmanned lunar and planetary expeditions and on establishing a permanent space station in earth orbit. The two goals Kennedy had set in 1961 were assured: an American would walk on the moon before the decade was out and ahead of the Russians.

Despite the appearance of success, Johnson bequeathed to Nixon a space program that had lost its purpose and its momentum. Even after three years of studies and recommendations, no important decisions about major projects for the 1970s had been made. During those same three years Johnson had had to cut more than a billion and a half dollars from NASA's budget. By June 1968, the number of workers employed by NASA in Southern California had declined to 60 percent of 1966 levels. During those same years, spending for the war escalated rapidly. And an unexpected downturn in the domestic economy in 1968 took huge bites out of federal revenues. In addition to NASA's cuts, $400 million were taken out of the Air Force MOL project, and its first launch was indefinitely delayed.

Beginning in 1968, the U.S. aerospace industry began a sharp decline of fortunes. The huge industry, which had sprouted and grown with the billions of federal dollars pumped into the missile and space programs in the 1960s, looked ahead to bleak times. The major missile systems had all been constructed, paid for, and deployed, and their assembly lines were shut down. With the arsenal of Thor, Jupiter, Minuteman, Atlas, and Polaris missiles already cocked and poised and the prevailing national spirit becoming decidedly antiwar, it was politically unreasonable to expect a new round of missile sales in the near future. Furthermore, the Apollo contracts had for the most part been filled, and in the absence of a vigorous post-Apollo program, new space orders were minimal. Furthermore, the declining domestic economy of the 1968 recession, coupled with the emergence of foreign competition in the aircraft industry, meant that fewer orders were being placed for commercial aircraft than the industry had expected. All of these factors combined to spell crisis for the aerospace industry. North American Rockwell executives were openly predicting that unless some major new space vehicle program was begun by 1972 at the latest (they had their sights on the space shuttle), the industry could face collapse. On Wall Street, aerospace stocks plummeted. Many of the workers who had built Apollo watched their spacecraft's successes from home, where they remained after being laid off.

Aerospace executives predicted a future without a missile industry and warned that national security could be jeopardized. Other industry observers expressed a more likely prospect: that the industry's giants would merge and further consolidate its enormous political and economic power into fewer and fewer anonymous hands. Some suggested that foreign investors might buy up large shares of the weakened industry, so that future military decisions could be influenced by foreign capitalists. The peace movement, which might have offered imaginative suggestions for conversion of the industry, lacked the power to place the issue of a peace-oriented conversion on the national agenda. It was left to the politicians to choose among space and missile options for something for the industry to do.

Less than three weeks after taking office, President Nixon issued a memorandum requesting recommendations on the direction which the U.S. space program should take in the post-Apollo period. He appointed a Space Task Group headed by Vice-President Spiro Agnew, who was also chairman of the National Space Council; Robert Seamans, former assistant NASA administrator and now Air Force secretary; Thomas Paine, the new NASA administrator; and Lee DuBridge, Nixon's science adviser. In July 1969, as the nation anxiously awaited the moon landing of Apollo 11, the task group issued its report, a political document that tried to please everyone while giving the president a choice between three levels of activity and expenditure. The most dramatic part of the report was a recommendation that the United States establish the goal of a manned expedition to Mars. No doubt this recommendation was made as a result of the success and popularity of NASA's Mariner probes, two of which were heading to Mars as the task group deliberated. The first of the task group's option packages included the establishment of a fifty-person space station in earth orbit, a reusable earth-to-space shuttle for the station, an earth-to-moon shuttle, a manned base on the moon, and an expedition to Mars in the early 1980s. The second-tier option would have built a smaller space station and a shuttle, abandoned the moon objective, and set off for Mars by the late 1980s. The final and simplest option called for a space station and shuttle, with the decision on when to go to Mars delayed. The common denominator of all the options was what had been the Air Force's minimal request for manned vehicles in the 1970s: a space station and shuttle. [1]

Nixon's Space Task Group—with the exception of Agnew, consisting of partisans of the space program listening to the testimony of fellow partisans sharing similar professional, military, and financial interests—presented what they presumably believed was a reasonable report. But Agnew's official announcement of the group's recommendation of a journey to Mars was met with incredulity, astonishment, and ridicule from Congress, the press, and the general public. The contrast between the confidence with which the report was presented and the disbelief with which it was received was a fair demonstration of the distance that had grown between the perceptions of the people in charge of the nation's space program and of the people who had to pay for them. The task group had expected that the moon landing would bolster popular support for space activity. They timed the release of their recommendations to occur as NASA basked in its greatest glory, but that wasn't enough.

Buzz Aldrin and Neil Armstrong landed Apollo 11's Eagle LEM (Lunar Excursion Module) on the moon's Tranquility Base on July 20, 1969. "One small step for man, one giant step for mankind," Armstrong said as he stepped onto the lunar surface. It was impossible not to be stirred by the occasion—footprints on the moon. "The footprint could mean, if we let it, that earthlings have done an unbelievably difficult and beautiful thing," Kurt Vonnegut wrote, but he doubted Americans would let it: He was certain they'd profane the symbol by using it to sell their products and their politicians.[2] Many people hoped that the accomplishment would become a new symbol to reestablish national purpose and pride that had been shattered by the Vietnam War.

President Richard Nixon, in a telephone call to the astronauts on the moon, said, "For every American this *has* to be the proudest day of our lives." Indeed, most Americans were awed by it—some no doubt were frightened. But many were also suspicious of what really was going on, who was getting rich off it, and why. There was something forced about much of it—for example, the flag that the astronauts placed there, which was made to appear as if it were flapping although the moon has no wind. As Norman Mailer later wrote, "NASA was heir to a chilling disease, for they had succeeded in making the moon dull."[3]

But the real emptiness of the Apollo gesture was not the groping for absent symbols that surrounded it, but the sense of climax about it when no one was certain what would come next. A giant step for mankind toward what? was the unanswered question. Richard Nixon's assertion that the moon landing was the greatest event since Creation implied that some new chapter for humanity was about to unfold. But most people, no matter what they felt about the event itself, sensed not only that the moon landing would fail to initiate a new era of manned space exploration with journeys to the planets and beyond, but that it probably would fail to generate even enough enthusiasm to guarantee any post-Apollo space program at all.

Despite all the crowing about the achievement, Apollo had long since served its primary purposes—getting a manned space program going, providing a suitable peaceful cover for military space activities, and giving a boost to the fledgling aerospace industry. The powers that mattered had long ago lost interest in the moon. The Air Force had given up its early ideas for a missile and reconnaissance base there by the early 1960s. The Defense Department was mostly interested in keeping the space program down in the strategically useful regions—below 10,000 miles altitude and at geostationary orbit.

The marriage of big money and a reachable, if dramatic goal had created a huge government program of space activity that would not have existed without it. In that way Apollo was a success. But its work had been done before its goal was reached, and that imparted a strange aura of anticlimax. It was not surprising that only a year later Neil Armstrong would be perplexed at how quickly people had forgotten and how few made note of the first anniversary. Even as the moon landing was being widely praised, there was virtually no political support for continuation of a NASA program at anywhere near the Apollo level.

But if the American flag on the moon failed to stir a new nationalism, the moon flights and NASA's earlier space flights *had* produced an image with powerful symbolic appeal: the "whole earth" as seen from space. A photograph of the floating planet appeared on the cover of a popular catalogue of the counterculture, *The Whole Earth Catalogue*. The picture became a poster with the caption "Love Your Mother." As Lucian had pointed out two thousand years earlier, the immense contrast between the infinities of the universe and the speck of cosmic dust known as Earth made the wars and cruelty on that little planet all the more horrible. Pictures from space provided visual proof of the fact that the earth is bounded, so its inhabitants can only foul its air and dirty its waters for so long. A picture of the earth appeared on the cover of *Only One Earth*, the report commissioned by the United Nations Conference on the Human Environment, which did much to raise the care and maintenance of the earth as a global issue of international concern. As the number of people concerned about the health of the planet grew, so too did the number of people objecting to the growing stockpiles of destructive weapons and the continuing planning for the ultimate environmental catastrophe: nuclear war. The photographs of the earth taken from space, photographs made possible only by the space program, provided powerful psychic weapons, undercutting the militarism and technocentrism that had been the very underpinnings of that same space program. It was not by coincidence that the first and very successful Earth Day sponsored by the new environmentalist movement occurred just months after the astronauts first walked on the moon.

All the major social movements of the time challenged the nation to turn its imagination and resources toward intrinsically earthbound projects—rebuilding the cities, restoring the health of the environment, and eliminating the social ailments of war, poverty, racism, and injustice. Two major criticisms of NASA were continually raised: in the press and in Congress. It was too expensive and too irrelevant to the concerns of the average tax-paying American. NASA's new assignment was clear: Come up with a future space program that would cost less and concentrate on technology for applications on earth.

In March 1970, nine months after the Future Space Programs Task

Group had issued its recommendations, Nixon responded: The Mars expedition was out. At the same time Nixon cut NASA's overall budget for fiscal year 1971 to its lowest level in ten years, while increasing the budgets for NASA's space station and shuttle programs. President Nixon's budget decisions meant that in the future NASA would primarily focus on near-earth space. In conjunction with the Air Force, NASA would develop the space station and shuttle the military wanted, but for which they had no immediate operational need. Nixon's emphasis should have been no surprise. He had run for president on a platform "deploring the lack of emphasis on the military use of space for America's defense." The two programs Schriever's Air Force Systems Command had been pushing for over ten years—the MOL space station and the X-20 Dyna-Soar reusable controlled reentry vehicle—were reborn as NASA's space station and shuttle.

As space scientists had warned for years, any exclusive focus on earth-orbiting vehicles would lead to NASA's being dominated by military interests. The Air Force's Project MOL, after six years of development and $1.3 billion spent, had been canceled and some of its missions reassigned to NASA's experimental space station, Skylab. Others were postponed to go aboard the eventual shuttle. It was easy to predict then that in future times of budgetary pressures when choices would have to be made, military considerations would prevail over space research.

NASA's original plans for the shuttle and space station had been part of a much grander vision of exploration. When NASA's plans went bust after Apollo, a coalition formed around the shuttle to keep NASA in the manned space flight business. The aerospace industry badly needed a new program and used its considerable political clout to get the shuttle program moving. Although NASA's shuttle designs, which had been in the works for years, would be capable of considerably less maneuverability and lateral glide mobility than had been planned for the X-20 Dyna-Soar, the Air Force agreed to join the shuttle program. In exchange the Air Force was accorded the power to dictate design changes to allow the shuttle to take off and land at the military space center, Vandenburg Air Force Base in California and carry the large payloads they projected they would need in the 1980s. On January 5, 1972, the president formally announced his support for the shuttle, "an entirely new transportation system designed to help transform the space frontier of the seventies into familiar territory, easily accessible for human endeavor in the 1980s and nineties."[4] Major shuttle contracts totaling

$5.5 billion were awarded to North American Rockwell and General Dynamics.

Next Congress had to be sold on the shuttle. Early in the campaign for political support, NASA administrators had determined that the best way to win congressional approval was to highlight the shuttle's potential cost savings in future space activities. NASA Associate Administrator Mrazek claimed that the shuttle would cut the costs of launching future satellites and other spacecraft by 90 percent. NASA hired a statistics corporation, Mathematica Incorporated, which conducted a study showing that the nation's space program would save around $12 billion over the next twenty years as a result of the shuttle program. The argument of cost efficiency, coupled with Air Force lobbying, convinced the Congress.

The major problem with the cost-savings argument was its assumption that the nation would have plenty to do in space once the shuttle was ready to provide transportation. The more the shuttle was used and reused, the more the cost per launch would decrease. Only a large increase in the scope of space activities would produce cost savings. By 1972, the military still had by far the most interest in utilizing earth-orbiting satellites. With the coming of the shuttle, they began projecting new things to do in space. The United States would need to think up entirely new things to do to exploit the shuttle's capabilities or be saddled with a future white elephant of enormous proportions.

The space shuttle's reusability, maneuverability, and large cargo bay promised, as Nixon pointed out, "to make space familiar territory, easily accessible for human endeavor in the 1980s and nineties." The shuttle would be able to carry up to 65,000 pounds to near-earth orbit, and with the upper-stage rocket being developed by the Air Force, up to 5,000 pounds to geostationary orbit. For the first time, a spaceship would be able to rendezvous with an orbiting satellite, retrieve it from space, and repair it or return it to earth. Furthermore, the shuttle would open up the possibility of eventually carrying materials and workers to build immense electronic systems in space. These included web like antennas so large that on earth they would collapse under their own weight; receivers so refined they could pick up weak signals from small, portable transmitters on earth; and complex data processing systems in orbit, relaying to small, mobile video display units the information transmitted by numerous and far-ranging sensors.

Even without in-space construction, the ability to launch greater numbers of larger, more expensive satellites from the shuttle promised to change the nature of satellite systems in a profound manner. Previously the expensive and complex receivers, transmitters, and data-processing equipment were all on earth, while satellites remained as small and simple as possible. If the complex part of the earth-space system was placed in orbit, then the ground equipment could be simple, portable, and widely dispersed. The commercial applications of this reversal, known in the space business as complexity inversion, were fairly obvious: satellite communications made available to everyone through cheap, commercially available ground equipment; home reception of direct-broadcast television, video telephones, and even Dick Tracy–like wrist radios. Other commercial applications of the shuttle's potential routinization of space activity included orbiting factories where industrial processes would take advantage of weightlessness and the near-perfect vacuum of space; solar power satellites taking advantage of continuous sunlight to collect and concentrate solar energy for later microwave transmission to earth receivers connected to the nation's power grids; and orbiting mirrors to reflect sunlight for night illumination of parts of the earth.

The potential commercial applications of space technology were used by the Nixon administration to justify space shuttle development and further NASA space activities. The more futuristic space industrialization proposals in particular would stir the public's imagination in the way that space exploration once had. Just as "peaceful space exploration" had been the motivating theme of the first era of space activities, commercialization, industrialization, and space colonization for the more adventurous became the motivating themes for the shuttle era.

The military implications of complexity inversion, though far less attractive, were far more real for the near future. The first use of remote-sensing devices—computerized command headquarters and automated killing—was already under way in the jungles of Vietnam and Laos. The linking of electronic battlefields into a global network via satellite merely awaited the technology and political decisions.

General Westmoreland, commander of U.S. forces in Southeast Asia, told a gathering of members of the Association of the U.S. Army in 1969 of a dream that he had based on his experience of electronic warfare in Vietnam.

I see battlefields or combat areas that are under twenty-four-hour real or near real-time surveillance of all types. I see battlefields on which we can destroy anything we locate through instant communications and almost instantaneous application of highly lethal firepower.

In summary, I see an Army built around an integrated area control system that exploits the advanced technology of communications, sensors, fire detection, and the required automatic data processing.[5]

Thirteen years later, U.S. military space engineers were busily turning Westmoreland's dream into a global reality. Well-protected war managers sitting in front of video display screens would direct distant wars, nuclear and nonnuclear alike, safely from a distance. In 1982, Richard DeLauer, U.S. undersecretary of Defense for Research and Engineering, wrote:

> Most of the public still perceives military might as represented primarily by guns, bombs, tanks, planes, ships, and missiles, and by those who use them.
>
> America's defense rests more on the ability to obtain strategic and tactical intelligence; to effectively control its resources over a *global battlefield*; to permit instantaneous communication with its operational forces, to simultaneously identify, and track a multitude of targets, under and on the sea, on the ground, in the air, or in space; to deliver appropriate munitions to these targets under any conditions, at any time, and with pinpoint accuracy; and finally, to subvert the effort of opposing forces to do the same. The means for accomplishing this are electronic systems that sense, transmit, compile, analyze, display, compare, store, and process information and then launch, guide, control, and trigger the various munitions carriers.[6]

The lessons military leaders believed they learned from the experience of Vietnam changed the tactics, strategies, and supporting technologies for use in future distant wars. Those lessons, along with changes in U.S. nuclear strategy, determined U.S. activity in space in the 1970s and 1980s.

12

Vietnam, the Electronic Battlefield, and U.S. Space Strategy

The events of 1961 and 1962—the Berlin crisis, and the Cuban missile crisis—had demonstrated to President Kennedy and Defense Secretary McNamara that there were no rational policy goals that could be achieved through the use of nuclear weapons; the result of their use would be too devastating. Every time the use of nuclear weapons was considered in the course of dealing with these crises it was rejected. The two superpowers demonstrated their unwillingness to risk a nuclear exchange. As one result, Soviet-American tensions began to ease by the summer of 1963. But at the same time America's involvement in Vietnam was escalating. As it appeared to Defense strategists, the nuclear stalemate could not be counted on to deter Communist expansion. America needed to shift its emphasis onto the so-called "wars of liberation" in the Third World. America was drawing the line with its military power in Southeast Asia.

One result of this change in emphasis was to give additional support to McNamara's opposition to the Air Force's proposed manned space and space weapons programs. They had little apparent relevance to the new international situation in which America found itself.

America's involvement in Vietnam ultimately affected all aspects of U.S. space activity. Research priorities were shifted away from long-term research on future strategic weapons and toward the short-term technology needs of a military force locked in jungle combat with an elusive enemy. Satellite systems for use by conventional forces took precedence over systems ultimately designed to fight in space. Later, as the war escalated, it resulted in increasing pressure being placed on NASA to justify its budget in view of the fact that the war and Great Society social programs were draining federal coffers. As the antiwar movement grew and evidence mounted that the government was deceiving the public about much of what was going on in Vietnam, space activities in general and the military space program in particular were met with increasing skepticism. And when the war was over, subsequent military space strategy became part of an overall strategy designed to avoid another Vietnam experience in the future.

By the early 1960s America's growing involvement in Vietnam forced the Defense Department research establishment to tailor its work to the needs of fighting jungle warfare against an elusive enemy. All areas of military research were affected. The Defense Advanced Research Projects Agency (DARPA), originally created by the Eisenhower administration to oversee military space research and development, gave top priority to electronic systems for counterinsurgency warfare. The Vietnamese guerrillas were familiar with the tropical terrain and could take advantage of it for the element of surprise when attacking and refuge when retreating. In order to overcome the enemy's advantages, large segments of America's research establishment were mobilized to provide the forces in Vietnam with electronic sensors that could "see" and "hear" in the jungle and with radio transmitters that could overcome the problems created by the dense jungle growth and its tendency to absorb the electromagnetic signals of normal military communications. Government scientists invented seismic sensors to feel the jungle floor for the evidence of guerrilla movement, metal detectors to pick up the presence of weapons, acoustic sensors to listen for the sound of voices and footsteps, infrared sensors capable of detecting the heat given off by a living body against the jungle background, and airborne infrared cameras capable of peering through cloud cover and at night.

Sensor technology, and the accompanying technology of information processing, gradually progressed toward remotely controlled warfare automation. The first sensor systems used in Vietnam consisted of seismic and acoustic detectors placed in a protective ring around U.S. jungle outposts and bases. They recorded what a guard on duty would normally fail to see and hear: distant activity that might signal an enemy approaching. Information gathered by remote sensors were transmitted to on-base terminals, where it was interpreted. As sensor technology grew more refined, and terminals more portable, foot soldiers carried the equipment on patrol. Airborne sensors were carried aboard helicopters and planes. As they grew still more refined, sensors were dropped along supply routes and other areas of suspected guerrilla activity. These were connected to distant terminals for processing and use by commanders in deciding where to direct what kind of force. The result was what the Army called the "Remotely Monitored Battlefield Sensors System," also known as the electronic battlefield.

America's growing reliance on electronic sensors and air power made a new approach to the fighting possible at a time when the Pentagon needed a strategy to reduce the number of men involved in direct combat. Through the mid-sixties the fighting in the countryside had grown increasingly deadly. The U.S. antiwar movement was growing in direct proportion to the number of GI corpses and the government's inability to justify the deaths to the American people. Electronic "force multipliers" allowed the Pentagon to reduce troop commitments while concurrently escalating the violence. As refined as the electronics of war became, peasants in the field created seismic disturbances on the ground similar to those made by guerrillas on patrol; herds of water buffalo gave off infrared body heat just as platoons of soldiers did; farmers' campfires were indistinguishable from soldiers'. All too frequently, bombers and helicopter gunships sent out in response to information provided by remote sensors resulted in civilian casualties.

President Nixon arrived at the White House with a promise to end American involvement in the war. To do this he escalated the automation of warfare that was already underway. In addition, in a process Nixon called "Vietnamization" of the war, he turned over the remaining ground action as much as possible to South Vietnamese government forces. As a result, American casualties were reduced. The need for a large infantry was also reduced and with it the need for a draft. By the early 1970s, America was apparently winding down its direct combat activities.

Even before the war was over, American strategists were contemplating how to avoid Vietnam-like conflicts in the future. At first, the reevaluation of U.S. military strategy focused on American commitments in Asia. But U.S. supported regimes in other parts of the world faced antigovernment guerrilla movements as well. A counterinsurgency strategy for Asia would be translatable around the globe. President Nixon first articulated a new strategy for Asia in a speech on the island of Guam on July 25, 1969. According to what would later be called the Nixon Doctrine, American policy would uphold three propositions as codified in Richard Nixon's 1970 report to Congress on U.S. foreign policy in the 1970s:

1. The United States will keep all its treaty commitments.
2. We shall provide a shield if a nuclear power threatens the freedom of a nation allied with us, or of a nation whose survival we consider vital to our security or to the security of the region as a whole.
3. In cases involving other types of aggression, we shall furnish military and economic assistance when requested and as appropriate. But we shall look to the nation directly threatened to assume the primary responsibility of providing the manpower for its defense.[1]

The Nixon Doctrine shifted emphasis away from direct U.S. intervention and toward arming and supporting the military forces of client states. While marking an apparent shift in U.S. Asia policy, the doctrine nonetheless repeated the same tragic flaw that marred each president's foreign policy since World War II: emphasizing military solutions to Third World instability. The same type of thinking had created the Vietnam tragedy. It failed to distinguish between foreign aggression and revolution. By defining almost all forces for radical change as Communist or Communist inspired, American foreign policy remained blind to the causes of Third World revolutions—poverty, oppression, inadequate or absent health care and other social services, grossly unequal distribution of land and wealth, hunger, and popular outrage over these conditions.

The Nixon Doctrine led to "Vietnamization" on a regional, and ultimately, a global level. The number of troops stationed worldwide was reduced. But the U.S. government promised to remain committed to its allies, and in cases where local forces were unable to prevail, the U.S. military would intervene rapidly and efficiently. A new type of force structure, one capable of rapid deployment from a distance, was required. It would have the ability to intervene militarily anywhere in the world, at the same time reducing troop commitments overseas and placating antiinterventionist sentiment at home. It was the globalization of the slogan "Firepower, not manpower."

Fundamentally, Nixon faced the same dilemma Eisenhower had faced upon entering office. In Korea, as in Vietnam, American forces, despite vast superiority in material resources, firepower, and technology, failed to achieve better than a bloody stalemate. Eisenhower was determined to extricate American troops from the war and evolve a foreign and military strategy to avoid another Korea. The Truman Doctrine had promised to use American military power to prevent

Communist expansion. But Eisenhower recognized that Truman's promise could require an immense worldwide military machine under constant mobilization, draining the U.S. economy and requiring a level of discipline from the American people inimical to the liberties they cherished. In response, the Eisenhower administration evolved the strategy of "massive retaliation," threatening the full weight of its nuclear might against a Communist invasion. But that too had proven inadequate, since a wide range of military activities fell somewhere between a recognizable invasion and internal civil war, for which massive retaliation was grossly inappropriate. Therefore, in the later years of his administration Eisenhower toyed with various strategies of "limited war." But they involved either the use of nuclear weapons on the battlefield, which could easily escalate into all-out nuclear war, or required the maintenance of worldwide conventional forces—something he rejected.

The Kennedy administration, after its first year and a half of unending crises, concluded that neither the Soviets nor the United States would risk a nuclear war as long as both sides were able to destroy the other in retaliation for a nuclear attack. Therefore, it placed greater emphasis on covert military activity and the building of a conventional army for counterinsurgency warfare. But that strategy led directly to Vietnam.

The Nixon administration added two new elements to the calculations—high-tech, "conventional" force and "flexible nuclear options." Where Eisenhower threatened massive nuclear retaliation, Nixon would back up local client forces with rapid, mobile conventional fire power for anything short of outright aggression by a nuclear-armed power. Nixon still threatened to use America's nuclear might to defend allies against an invasion. But the administration rejected massive retaliation as the only nuclear option and refused to accept the notion of "mutually assured destruction." Instead, Nixon and Defense Secretary Melvin Laird made it official military doctrine that the armed forces be prepared for a number of nuclear options. They accepted the argument certain nuclear strategists had been making for years: that the president should not be locked into one massive nuclear targeting plan but instead should have options, including strikes against Soviet military targets alone, limited battlefield nuclear strikes, and targets selected to be hit as a warning of what might follow. The military would require increases in both the quantity of weapons and the quality of targeting, communications, and surveillance in order to provide the president with these nuclear options.

The strategies of flexible nuclear options and rapid deployment of conventional forces increased the importance of military space systems and placed severe technological requirements on them. Beginning with the formulation of the Nixon Doctrine and continuing through the 1970s, America's operational force structure became progressively more dependent on military space systems. There were five primary reasons for this: the U.S. decision to maintain the ability to rapidly intervene in remote military theaters of its choosing; the progressive loss of overseas bases, resulting in greater need for intercontinental C^3 systems; increasing needs for intelligence information from around the world; increased demands on ICBM guidance for precise strikes against selected targets and equally stringent requirements for over-the-horizon missile guidance of advanced conventional warheads; and finally, a perpetuating cycle of increasing performance, leading to new strategies, increasing demands on performance, etc. In addition, as operational forces came to depend on space support, military satellites became ever more attractive targets. Therefore, antisatellite weaponry and satellite defense received correspondingly increased attention. The Nixon Doctrine, and subsequent strategies intended to prevent revolutionary change in the Third World, gave the military race in space a new impetus. Eventually, the race took on a relentless quality that gave it the appearance of being separate from earthbound policy. But, in fact, space research and development has always taken its cue from U.S. global military strategy and, in particular, changes in nuclear doctrine.

The first such doctrine, that of massive retaliation, followed when only the United States possessed atomic weapons. It relied on America's bomber force to carry it out. Orbiting satellites were conceived of primarily as a future method of high-altitude surveillance, identifying and locating targets for the Strategic Air Command. And so the first satellite study projects, begun in the late 1940s, concentrated on reconnaissance and surveillance. The feasibility of aerospace bombers was also under study.

In the early 1950s the emergence of the Soviet Union as a second nuclear power forced changes in nuclear doctrine. The apparent Soviet emphasis on large booster rockets for long-range missiles pushed the

United States to emphasize the same. Intercontinental missile warfare would involve distant enemies using weapons that traveled above the atmosphere at meteoric speeds. Only via a vantage point in space could such warfare be managed. The amount of attention given to military space activities increased accordingly. Now, in addition to reconnaissance and surveillance, satellites were called upon to locate and measure Soviet air defense radar, assess and record Soviet radio transmissions, provide navigational information to the submarine fleet, relay communications from command centers to bombers and missile silos, measure geomagnetic anomalies that might affect missile-firing accuracy, and provide warning of a Soviet missile attack. If satellites were now designed to participate in a global war, they would also have to be defended. Likewise, enemy satellites would become important targets. All of these tasks became necessary when America lost its monopoly on atomic weapons and the means to deliver them. They led to the proliferation of military space projects that so complicated the adoption of a national space policy in the second Eisenhower administration. The difficulty in establishing a space policy mirrored Eisenhower's inability to choose a nuclear strategy to replace the massive retaliation that had lost credibility in the face of a possible Soviet retaliation in kind.

In the first years of the Kennedy administration, Secretary of Defense McNamara adopted a strategy of "damage limitation." Accordingly, the U.S. would focus on such means as antiballistic missile systems, civil defense networks, and counterforce targeting of Soviet missiles and bombers in order to limit to acceptable levels the damage expected to result from a nuclear exchange. A damage-limitation strategy, it was hoped, would return credibility to America's threat of a nuclear response to a Soviet invasion (using conventional forces) of Western Europe or the Middle East. But damage limitation would also place exceptional stress on military technology and military budgets. ABMs required tremendous tracking, pointing, and aiming techniques. Counterforce targeting required advances in photoreconnaissance techniques and satellite navigation and guidance. And there was no guarantee that in a nuclear war damage would be significantly limited by these means.

In 1963, Secretary McNamara backed away from damage limitation and articulated the concept of mutually assured destruction—MAD. MAD strategy recognized that nuclear offense would always be simpler and cheaper than defense against nuclear attack. It was impossible to ensure that the Soviets would be incapable of getting through America's defenses with the capacity to make a nuclear exchange unbearably destructive. The assumption of MAD was that, as long as both the United States and the USSR were assured that starting a nuclear war meant signing their own death sentences as viable societies, both would be unwilling to initiate hostilities.

In the MAD era, damage limitation was out. Instead, military policy was directed toward assuring that America's retaliatory capability would remain sufficiently destructive to deter a Soviet attack. All forms of satellite reconnaissance—electronic, infrared, and photographic— were required to ensure that the United States could outsmart Soviet defenses. Emphasis was placed on early warning satellites to protect against a Soviet counterforce attack. And with the signing of the test ban treaty, a new series of satellites came into being that could detect nuclear explosions in the atmosphere and in space.

The adoption of the MAD doctrine prevented, for a short period, the proliferation of the complex nuclear war strategies that came later under the rubric of flexible options. It freed the Defense Department to focus attention on conventional and counterinsurgent war. Satellite systems relevant to conventional military operations—surveillance, navigational aids, and communications relay—became the space systems of prime concern.

When the Nixon administration shifted nuclear and conventional military policy once again, U.S. space priorities followed. Yet, although military policy usually set technology requirements, this was not a simple demand-response relationship. Frequently, developments in space technology made a new military strategy possible. By the late 1960s, in all the major satellite tasks, improvements were resulting in new military possibilities.

In communications, the technology had progressed from the first foil-covered sphere, named Relay, backscattering carefully directed radio beams earthward, to the first geostationary satellites with on-board transponders capable of amplifying the weakened signals it received for return transmission the 20,000 miles back to earth. The first geostationary satellites were planned in the late fifties by the Defense Advanced Research Projects Agency under Project Advent. The idea of Advent was to place three or four large satellites in stationary orbit, thus establishing point-to-point communication worldwide for control of bombers, submarines, and spacecraft. NASA had taken over the experimental communications work, and the first comsats to achieve geostationary orbit were NASA's Syncom I and II, launched in July 1963. The first operational military comsats in a geostationary orbit were launched by the Air Force in 1966. Worldwide point-to-point communications were possible for the first time. However, the usefulness of comsats in geostationary orbit was limited by the immense distances information had to travel. Powerful transmitters were necessary to reach the satellites, and large antennae were needed to receive messages. Such large equipment would be vulnerable to enemy countermeasures. And the necessary equipment would be too bulky to have the mobility required in wartime situations. But geostationary satellites, remaining as they do in a fixed position relative to the earth, are ideal for maintaining continuous communications.

The ideal geostationary comsat for improving C^3 in a conventional war situation would carry jamproof transponders so powerful that they could link together widely dispersed, mobile ground units carrying small transmitters and receivers. The prototype for such satellites were the Advanced Technology Satellites (ATS) developed jointly by NASA and the Defense Department. The first Defense ATS and four other Air Force comsats were placed in stationary orbit at the same time, on July 1, 1967.

The first satellite designed specifically for use in counterguerrilla warfare, TACSAT, was launched on February 9, 1969. As Major Thomas Winter explained in *Military Review*, "Special forces teams, in a friendly country with a potential insurgency situation, could cover the entire country through a network of team pack TacSat terminals located at strategic hamlets or villages. This type of system is particularly useful when the national telecommunications system is limited or nonexistent." [2] Theoretically, it would also be possible to link remote seismic and acoustic sensors with TACSAT or similar transmitters located throughout a disputed area. Heat-seeking or other "smart" weapons could then be targeted from afar at anything that moves. In this way, an area could be controlled without any commitment of human soldiers. International border patrol could be mechanized in a similar manner.

Navigation satellites followed a similar pattern of development toward increasing accuracy and greater numbers of small, mobile receivers on earth. Transit, the first operational navigation satellite system, was used by the Navy, including its Polaris ballistic missile submarines. A properly equipped submarine or surface ship could use Transit's signal to calculate its longitude and latitude within 200-yard accuracy. But Transit's operational utility was limited to large vessels carrying the heavy equipment needed to receive Transit's signal and by the fact that a navigator could only update his position once in ninety minutes while waiting for another satellite to come within signal range.

By 1965 the Defense Department was projecting a vastly improved satellite navigation system that could be used not only by large naval vessels, but also by air and artillery units in "tactical limited war situations." According to McNamara's Defense Director of Research and Engineering, Harold Brown, who described the system in hearings before the Senate Space Sciences Committee, the proposed navigation system would allow close coordination between multiple air and artillery units shooting at the same target. It would assist transport units in the accurate spot landing of troops, supplies, and artillery. And it would improve targeting accuracy of short-range tactical ballistic missiles fired over the horizon.[3] By the 1970s this proposed system had expanded to become a "global positioning system" to eventually include twenty-four satellites providing continuous worldwide navigation information to any user carrying the portable Navstar receiver.

Satellite surveillance and reconnaissance also grew progressively more sophisticated. Throughout the 1960s, U.S. intelligence was aided by low-flying, close-inspection photoreconnaissance satellites with a film ejection system and a separate surveillance satellite system transmitting wide-area video pictures to receiving stations on the ground. By 1971, these separate reconnaissance and surveillance tasks were combined in one satellite, known as "Big Bird" because of its large winglike configuration. Each Big Bird satellite carried two separate camera systems and was also capable of launching separate electronic reconnaissance subsatellites. Big Bird's close-up optics reportedly could take such clear pictures from space that intelligence analysts could distinguish one person's facial features from another's. In addition, Big Bird flew in a higher orbit than the early photoreconnaissance satellites and therefore continued operating for months where previous systems lasted days.

Electronic reconnaissance or "ferreting" satellites progressed from recording powerful Soviet air defense radar signals to recording and retransmitting radio and telecommunications, and reportedly even telephone conversations.

With these refinements in satellite capabilities, space technology was marching inexorably toward "real-time" operations. There was a steady decrease in the amount of time it took for satellites to gather information, for ground stations to receive it, for computers to process it, for personnel to analyze it, and for decision makers to act on it. The first generation of operational military satellites provided worthwhile information concerning enemy targets and enemy strengths, weather conditions and predictions, and other useful details, but because of delays in receiving and processing information from space it was of limited value during the course of an actual conflict. In fact, because of their limitations early military satellites were not normally considered threats to America's commitment to the peaceful use of outer space. But as satellite capabilities developed, the distinction between support functions and actual combat functions began to blur. Satellites became integrated into the functioning of particular weapons, becoming for all intents and purposes weapons in space. A satellite locating and identifying a target and triggering a so-called "munitions carrier" is as much a part of the overall weapon as the rifle's sight and trigger are part of the rifle.

As satellites were integrated into both nuclear and conventional weapons systems, greater priority was placed on assuring their survivability during a war. With the Nixon administration's shift from MAD to a doctrine of flexible nuclear options, satellite systems now would be required to be able to perform during an ongoing nuclear war. In order to assure continued functioning during the length of the war, satellites would require vast new operational and protective characteristics that were previously unnecessary. The military would now want to protect their satellites from a variety of forms of attack. They would want the ability to quickly launch satellites during the war to replace those destroyed. They would want spare satellites and redundant communications channels at jam-resistant frequencies. They would want to replace vulnerable solar-power panels with powerful on-board nuclear generators they could protect. They would want new kinds of launch pads, hidden and defensible, such as underground silos and submarines. Though such requirements were well beyond the financial, political, and technical means at hand, the groundwork was laid for the emergence of hardened, survivable space systems in the 1980s.

The Vietnam war had forced the military to emphasize operational systems in its research and planning. However, most of those systems did not mature in time to be of use in the war. And ironically, although the emphasis had been toward combat operations and away from futuristic manned vehicles and space weapons, the growing importance of space in earth combat renewed interest in space as a separate field of operations with its own vehicle and weapons requirements.

By the early 1970s, the United States had begun to set up the first-generation electronic network for managing military operations on a global scale. A few years later, improved versions of the component satellites were being placed in orbit. Both space powers were improving the means to attack enemy spaceships. Civilian space endeavors became a small fraction of the world's total activity in space. And yet at the same time the most promising efforts yet made to bring about international cooperation in space between the United States and the Soviet Union were occurring.

13

Apollo-Soyuz and the Promise of International Cooperation

Every historical development results from a confusing mix of often contradictory forces. Many of the same forces turning America's space program away from exploration toward technology applications and ultimately to increased militarization were, at the same time, creating the possibility for a truly international approach to the development of space technology for the benefit of all. The Apollo landing marked the end of the U.S.-Soviet moon race, with its accompanying competitive pressures. Throughout the period from 1962 to the landing in 1969, dissenting voices had been raised against what many believed was needless and foolish competition. But despite a brief period in 1963 when the superpowers seemed to be about to agree on a joint lunar expedition, competition prevailed over cooperation.

However, as the race came to an end, and the United States emerged the victor, pressures against future joint manned flight diminished. Just months prior to the moon landing, the United States and the Soviet Union reached an agreement on mutual cooperation in the event of a need to rescue astronauts in space. If cooperation in a joint rescue was to be feasible, then either nation's vehicles would need mutually compatible docking equipment and techniques. In April 1970 the Soviets' Academy of Sciences proposed that bilateral talks begin on future space cooperation. In October the two nations agreed to develop compatible docking systems and to continue talks on other forms of cooperation. The following June, NASA and the Soviet Academy of Sciences opened talks to consider a joint Apollo-Soyuz mission.

The opening of Apollo-Soyuz talks encouraged hope that an arms race in space would be avoided. With both nations publicly shifting the emphasis of their space programs to manned earth-orbiting vehicles, what they did "up there" was increasingly important. By 1970 the likelihood had grown that within a few years there would be two manned orbiting space stations. The Soviet Union had announced in 1968 that they did not intend to land a man on the moon. Instead the emphasis would be on the establishment of a space station. The United States had officially been planning since 1965 to orbit a manned military space station—unofficially since the late 1950s.

The Air Force's Project MOL had been intended to study the space station's feasibility for surveillance and wartime C^3. But by 1969, satellite robotics had already advanced to the point where the Air Force was hard pressed to define a mission for MOL that couldn't be done better and cheaper by the new, advanced reconnaissance system, Big Bird, and Defense Satellite Communications systems.

When MOL was canceled in 1969, NASA proposed a civilian replacement as part of its attempt to identify earth-orbital missions for Apollo technology, a program known as the Apollo Application Program (AAP). Since more Apollo spacecraft had been built than would be used by the lunar exploration missions, there would be leftovers for other uses. Apollo could be outfitted for space station use in combination with a large cylindrical laboratory, much the same as the original MOL configuration, which had been based on the Gemini module. The AAP space station became known as Skylab, a joint NASA–Air Force project.

Skylab and the Soviet's Salyut space station both claimed scientific research objectives in astronomy, biomedicine, in-orbit materials processing, surveys of earth resources, and creation of launch platforms for future interplanetary flight. Since their purposes were the same and of interest to space scientists worldwide, it seemed reasonable that the nations cooperate. Some even suggested that the programs be united into a United Nations space station. Talk of Salyut/Skylab cooperation quickly vanished, however, when the first three cosmonauts to visit the Salyut station in June 1971 were found dead in their capsules upon their return from three weeks in space. They had suffocated when air leaked out a faulty valve in their spaceship. The Soviets abandoned their first Salyut station, and the program was delayed a year. Détente was evident at the funeral—an American astronaut who would later command the Apollo spaceship in the Soviet-American flight, Thomas Stafford, was among the pallbearers at the state funeral in Moscow.

In 1971, détente was at its peak. In September, the United States and the Soviet Union signed the first Strategic Arms Limitation Talks

(SALT) agreements. It was the first time that arms limitation talks had actually led to an agreement. Full of complicated formulas and definitions, the agreements did not in fact ban or dismantle a single weapon. In fact, the "limitations" were set well above the stockpiles current in both nations. The SALT agreements were more a gentlemen's agreement to play the next round of the arms race according to rules. In effect, as disarmament critics noted, it legitimized the nuclear arms buildup. As part of the SALT agreements, both nations agreed not to interfere with each other's "national technical means of verification," which meant reconnaissance and surveillance satellites. It was the first time in history that two nations agreed to allow spying on each other, a tacit recognition that the age of satellites was here.

In the same period, the early 1970s, the United Nations took up the issues raised by earth's resource surveillance satellites. NASA had begun looking into the commercial applications of the surveillance techniques first developed by the military. The first of the ERTS (Earth Resources Technology Satellites) began operating in 1971. The military would only allow NASA to have surveillance capabilities of far lower quality and photographic power than was available to the Air Force. Still, there were a number of tasks the ERTS were expected to perform, such as identifying likely deposits of minerals and oil, tracking water flow and crop growth, pinpointing sources of water and air pollution, and taking forest and wildlife inventories. NASA satellites in low earth orbit would carry multispectral cameras, beam the information to ground receiving stations, and eventually process the data into finished pictures. The pictures were made available to anyone willing to buy them. The major oil and mining companies, who could expend the resources in learning how to identify geological formations that indicated reserves, stood to reap the most dramatic benefits. Speculators in crop futures would also find ERTS data profitable, using them to predict yields.

Many Third World nations expressed concern that ERTS (also known as LANDSAT) data would be exploited by multinational corporations with far greater access to development capital than the nation under whose land the resources lay. The suggestion was made by the Soviet Union and others that the United Nations establish a center for the collection and distribution of ERTS data, thereby allowing member nations some control over the dissemination of information about their resources. Brazil, with the support of a number of other Third World nations, proposed a treaty restricting the rights of space powers to collect and dispense information about a nation without its consent. But NASA policy under the Nixon administration took a cavalier laissez-faire attitude, insisting on the right of open access to ERTS data. According to the new Nixon space philosophy, which stressed the commercial applications of space technology, ERTS was to become the second profitable venture in space, after commercial satellites for TV broadcast and communications.

Although the ERTS issue was controversial, it demonstrated some of the international character of satellite activity and involved the United Nations at least in considering a role in the future organization of space activities. In conjunction with the Soviet-American cooperation in preparation for an Apollo-Soyuz mission, hopes were raised for making space a truly peaceful international environment.

America had adopted a free-enterprise philosophy toward space— one that has dominated the U.S. civilian space program ever since— which ran counter to the interests of national sovereignty for the people of the rest of the world. It eventually isolated the United States from the considered opinion of nearly every other nation, insofar as space activities went. In addition, it stood in ironic contradiction to the very nature of space applications.

ERTS is a perfect example of this contradiction. Satellite cameras can cover broad areas, continuously over time, and pick up changes and patterns that go unnoticed on the ground. They yield useful information about a watershed, but not a stream; land use patterns, but not a farmer's field. In order for a nation to make use of such information, a strong central government is required, capable of making effective economic decisions regarding the nation's agriculture, timberlands, water, and energy and mineral resources. In the Third World, such effective national governments have been consistently undermined, first by European colonialism, and later by American and European corporations seeking freedom from government control in exchange for their capital investment. Where strong national governments do exist, tensions with foreign investors are often strongest when it comes to issues of national resource exploitation, exactly the area where ERTS data is most useful.

The central issue in the future of space was already apparent in the ERTS debate: Since all space activities are planet-spanning, how can they be organized to serve the needs of the planet as a whole? By siding with private enterprise against the interests of national sovereignty and Third World development, the United States clearly established a policy supporting the expansion of the global power of the multinational corporations. In the Space Age, the planet appears to be inexorably moving toward greater interdependence and more transnational forms of decision making. If the planet becomes more organized it will either occur through international agencies representing cooperative efforts of many nations, multinational corporations representing the interests of investors, or some organizational forms representing temporary compromises between the multitude of conflicting interests. The struggle to determine the organization and management of global resources will likely be the central struggle of international relations in the twenty-first century. And the development and use of space technology may well play the determining role in that struggle.

Soviet-American military competition and an arms race in space would undermine the chances for international cooperation in space and on earth. On the other hand, Soviet-American cooperation in space might just be the first step toward international cooperation on earth. In the context of the early 1970s, there was much more at stake than just the docking of two spaceships as the Soviets and Americans planned their first joint space mission.

July 15, 1975, was the eve of the thirtieth anniversary of the world's first atomic explosion at Alamagordo, New Mexico. On that day three American astronauts and two Soviet cosmonauts were separately launched on the world's first international rendezvous and docking mission. The mission was successful. The men exchanged gifts and handshakes and visited each other's cabins before returning to earth in their separate spaceships. The coincidence of the atomic anniversary and the Apollo-Soyuz mission was noted by a *New York Times* editorial, which expressed hope that "Soviet American détente is only the beginning toward more broadly based cooperation in space efforts involving the personnel and talents of every nation for the benefit of all humanity."[1]

The choice in space was clear: either space would become more internationalized, with appropriate international bodies evolving to manage and control the development, or space would become an arena of greater competition and eventually conflict.

At first it seemed as if the Apollo-Soyuz mission would, in fact, be a new beginning in space. Even as the astronauts were visiting each other through their jointly designed docking units, plans were proceeding toward further joint flights and exchange of ground receiving equipment in order to make it possible for each nation to receive data directly from the other's earth resources surveillance satellites. Apollo astronaut Deke Slayton suggested that the next joint mission be held aboard the soon-to-be-unveiled space shuttle.

But despite the potent symbolism of Apollo-Soyuz and the clear, rational arguments favoring increased international space cooperation, the mission, like so many other apparent beginnings in the curious history of space flight, turned out to be a weak conclusion rather than the beginning of a new era of cooperation. Just as Neil Armstrong's one small step turned out to foreshadow the end of manned space exploration for a while, so too, the Apollo-Soyuz mission marked the end of a brief flirtation with the notion of Soviet-American teamwork in space. Nothing much happened in the afterglow of the mission; space cooperation fell victim to the usual Soviet xenophobia and secrecy and American anti-Soviet hostility.

Critics of the mission in the United States charged that the Soviets had received invaluable information about American technology. Apollo was the superior ship, these critics argued, and America could learn nothing from Soyuz. Apollo had had to do all the work in the rendezvous, while Soyuz just stayed in its parking orbit and waited—and then received half the credit. These critics managed to place the mission in a perspective of competitive gains and losses and thereby ensured that the vital issues of international cooperation in space would be left out of the discussion.

Defenders of the mission responded by assuring the critics that neither side had gained any really useful information. After all, the mission was the last use of the Apollo spacecraft and the Saturn rocket, both out-of-date systems already ten years old. As for the Soyuz craft, U.S. astronauts and technicians involved in the mission reported that it was comparable in technological and engineering sophistication to the old two-person Gemini spacecrafts of the early 1960s. Therefore, its defenders claimed, the mission posed no threat to national security.

Some, including Apollo Commander Stafford, insisted that the Americans had gained a unique insight into Soviet space operations. Using the vocabulary of espionage, Stafford, who would one day become the head of Air Force space weapons research, later insisted that the astronauts "had a unique experience in working with the Apollo-Soyuz program. Our embassy told us that we had penetrated Soviet society deeper than any group since World War II," [2] exactly the kind of statement to give support to suspicious and distrustful elements within the Kremlin.

No astute observer could fail to see that there was no future for a cooperative international program defended for its uselessness and promoted for the espionage advantage it provided. Obviously, the mission was meant as merely a symbolic gesture for everyone involved. But it was a symbol that fell flat in 1975. It was by then three years after the peak of détente, and the first steps in the new space arms race were already being taken. But though the spacefaring superpowers retreated from cooperation and proceeded toward arming the heavens, the issue of international cooperation for the benefit of all would not go away. As the arms race prepared to leap into space in the late 1970s and early 1980s, the moral and political issues of space were more starkly evident than ever.

14

The Mid-Seventies:
Militarization Completed

The militarization of Soviet and American space activities was nearly completed by the mid-1970s, undercutting the chances for cooperation. Each nation focused its program on somewhat different priorities. In the United States, NASA was absorbed in its joint venture, with the Air Force developing the U.S. Space Shuttle while the U.S. Defense Department focused on operating and improving America's electronic command and control communications, and its intelligence (C^3) network. The Soviet space program emphasized the further development of its manned space station and their goal of maintaining a permanent presence in space. It was widely believed that Soviet astronauts carried out routine space surveillance from the station, and may have been experimenting with components of future space weapons.

In addition to their Salyut space station, the Soviets now had a complete network of military satellites similar to but less sophisticated than America's. They also continued development on a co-orbiting "killer satellite" ASAT system, while the Americans dismantled their ground-launched direct-assent ASATs. For the first time since the onset of the Cold War the Soviets outpaced the United States in a number of space and missile developments. It is widely accepted that by the end of the 1970s the Soviets reached strategic military parity with the West. The long period of American superiority, begun with the atomic monopoly of the postwar years and peaking in the early 1960s, came to an end. The loss rekindled the rhetorical fervor of America's cold warriors, which had quieted during the brief period of Soviet-American détente.

Not that the Americans were merely waiting for the space shuttle. Primary attention was given to the space segment of the military C^3I network. In 1973 the Nixon administration approved the Navigation System using Timing and Ranging (NAVSTAR), also known as the Global Positioning System (GPS). NAVSTAR was conceived of as a multipurpose navigation system for both military and civilian users. Its military importance would be paramount. Any vehicle equipped with a NAVSTAR receiver set would receive continuous information, locating its position within fifty feet, measuring its velocity within inches per second, and providing a precise time reference. Artillery and rocket units could locate themselves precisely during target acquisition. Bombers and missiles could evaluate en route navigation and make necessary course corrections. Supply planes could make accurate airdrops at night and in bad weather. Cruise missiles could be guided to target. Bombers from dispersed bases could rendezvous and coordinate missions. NAVSTAR would become an invaluable "force multiplier" when operational, since positioning accuracy is crucial for nearly all missions.

NAVSTAR plans originally called for twenty-four satellites circling the globe in three rings. In 1973, the system was projected to be operational by 1984 at a total cost of $1.7 billion. (At this writing, it is now scheduled for operational use in the late 1980s with six fewer satellites and at a cost of almost $9 billion.)

Beginning with the Initial Defense Communications Satellite Project (IDCSP), satellites that were operational in geostationary orbit by 1970, the point-to-point communications links required for the management of a global military force were in place. Instantaneous centralized command and control were made possible. As a result, more and more decisions were made by distant authorities. The successful deployment of the IDCSP permitted the centralization of command over the fighting in Vietnam at the Pentagon, and increasingly in Henry Kissinger's office. Control of the air war in the north was moved out of regional American headquarters in Saigon and given to U.S. Air Command authorities in Hawaii. The centralization of global command and control placed tremendous demands on communications. Satellite communications systems became the most important element in the military space program.

A separate communications system was created to relay the messages of nuclear war—warnings from the early warning satellites to the military authorities and orders from the National Command Authorities to the retaliatory forces. The Air Force Satellite Communications (AFSATCOM) system, the first such system specifically designed to maintain communications with the nuclear forces, was first tested in 1975. The system relied on ultrahigh frequency (UHF) channels capable of very low data rates—just enough to carry the Emergency Action Messages in short teletyped instructions.

Before AFSATCOM achieved initial operational capability on May 22, 1979, the Carter-Brown Defense Department adjusted its nuclear war–fighting doctrine. Complex new demands were placed on the nation's strategic communications. AFSATCOM was a low-speed teletype system for carrying the Emergency Action Message. It was created to transmit the message to retaliate. It could not receive damage estimates, or maintain control over subsequent military action for the duration of an extended nuclear war. The desire to present options to the president, such as "flexible response" and "limited retaliation" in the event of nuclear war, created huge design headaches for SATCOM engineers.

A single nuclear blast in space saturates thousands of cubic miles with large doses of gamma radiation, charged-particle radiation, and neutrons traveling unimpeded through the vacuum of space. The result of many nuclear blasts occurring in space simultaneously is merely a matter of conjecture, since the situation has never occurred.

There are many ways to enhance a satellite's chance of surviving nuclear effects. Most simply, a satellite can be shielded by heavy metals. But shielding greatly increases the weight of a satellite, and therefore its launch and operation costs, and still won't protect it from the irradiated metals' release of secondary X-rays, nor the electromagnetic pulse generated within the electronics. These indirect effects can erase computer memories and burn out satellite circuits. Specially designed cables can be fabricated from materials with fewer available electrons, thereby decreasing the problem of emissions and X-rays. Particularly vulnerable circuits can be backed up by multiple spares, increasing the chances of endurance. Extra satellites can be stored in orbit with their power turned off and therefore less susceptible to electronic damage by radiation. They would await command from earth to turn on after their partners have been destroyed.

Solar energy panels, which are deployed like giant wings outside a satellite, are particularly vulnerable to radiation effects. These can be replaced by on-board plutonium batteries or small nuclear power generating plants. All the radiation-hardening techniques add considerably to the cost of the military space program, and none is certain to work under actual war conditions.

By the late 1970s, only the AFSATCOM strategic communications satellites had incorporated nuclear hardening into their design. But then the distinction between nuclear and conventional forces began to break down under the nuclear doctrine articulated by Presidents Carter and Reagan. Priority was then given to hardening all the elements of the C^3I network.

The effect of nuclear blasts was only the most extreme threat facing orbiting satellites. By the 1970s, military technology had progressed toward operational antisatellite weapons and offensive electromagnetic countermeasures.

Antisatellite weapons (ASATs) had been under consideration in the United States in one form or another since at least 1956, when the first spy satellite contracts were awarded. The first study contracts for ASATs were awarded shortly thereafter. In the late 1950s, a whole range of ASAT options were considered. They included ship-launched, ground-launched, and air-launched missiles, and satellite interceptors.

The McNamara Defense Department settled on a ground-launched system that involved the same basic guidance and interception technology as antiballistic missiles. The ground-launched ASAT carried a nuclear warhead that would explode in space in the general vicinity of the target. This system was deployed from 1962 until 1975 in the South Pacific. By the early 1970s, with the U.S. military growing increasingly reliant on space assets, the ground-launched ASAT system fell into disfavor. Because of the effects of nuclear explosions in space, any nuclear ASAT attack on Soviet targets might also damage or destroy U.S. satellites at the same time.

The Soviet Union tested an orbiting satellite interceptor in 1968, and by the early 1970s their system was deployed. With the Soviet ASAT, a "killer satellite" would be launched into an orbital configuration similar to its target's, where it would maneuver near to the target and explode into a shower of shrapnel.

In the summer of 1975, the United States revived development of an air-launched ASAT. It would involve the firing of miniature heat-seeking missiles by a small two-stage rocket released from the belly of a high-altitude F-15 fighter. The new American ASAT, projected for tests by the early 1980s, would signify a major escalation in the space arms race. Unlike a co-orbiting interceptor, it could strike from anywhere without warning. One of the last acts of Gerald Ford's administration was to grant presidential approval to the development of this new ASAT.

The 1976 elections returned the Democrats to the White House after an eight-year absence. Harold Brown, former director of Defense Research and Engineering under McNamara, and later his Air Force secretary, became secretary of Defense under President Carter. In the McNamara Defense Department, Brown had confronted those he called "enthusiasts for space wars" over the issues of space weapons and manned military space vehicles. Now, in 1976, the Air Force was well on its way to having a manned vehicle through its participation in the space shuttle project, and an ASAT arms race was underway.

McNamara and Brown had put forward three arguments in opposing the more exotic military space schemes. At the time of Harold Brown's return to the Pentagon, those arguments remained cogent. First, the United States had always been, and still was, more active in the military use of space than the Soviets. For both technological and geostrategic reasons, the United States had come to rely on its space assets for wide-ranging military operations. The Rapid Deployment Force (one of Brown's major concerns) and future operations in the Mideast and Asia would be even more dependent on satellites for C^3I. On the other hand, the Soviets were less dependent than the Americans on their satellites. Their electronic and robotic technology was comparatively primitive, making satellite C^3I more difficult; and their forces were located close to the regions they considered strategic, making satellite C^3I less essential. Any tit-for-tat ASAT exchange would wind up costing the Americans far more dearly than the Soviets. Therefore, it was in America's interest to avoid active conflict in space. Since the weapons of spacewar were not yet deployed, it might be possible to avoid an arms race in space. Second, there would be no end to a space arms race once begun. It would be astoundingly expensive. The need to defend satellites against ASAT attack would result in rising costs along the entire spectrum from satellite design engineering to operations. The most crucial satellites would need to be defended against a host of imaginable new types of offense. If space were to become an arena of active conflict, the number of conceivable weapons and antiweapons would be as vast as anyone's "star wars" imagination could make it. Third, the international consensus rejecting claims of sovereignty in space might break down over the issues of militarization. The first such breakdown occurred when the Declaration of Bogotá was signed in December 1976 by eight equatorial nations. Claiming that geostationary orbits are scarce natural resources, the eight equatorial nations—Brazil, Colombia, Congo, Ecuador, Indonesia, Kenya, Uganda, and Zaire—declared that since the geostationary orbital plane passed over the equator it was subject to their sovereignty. Other Third World and European nations were likely to become increasingly vocal in their objection to the expropriation of space for the military advantage of the superpowers.

But despite these convincing arguments against initiating a space arms race with the Soviets, the pressures to proceed were strong. A powerful and organized group of cold warriors argued that in whatever field the United States possessed technological superiority it should be developed and exploited for military advantage.

In the Cold War of the 1950s, this same grouping of interests had rallied around the Air Force's long-term program to exploit space technology for military superiority. But even this group had to come to terms with the fact that "superiority" was meaningless in the age of nuclear weapons when even the inferior combatant held the power to reduce its enemies to radioactive debris. By the mid 1970s, however, the advances in targeting and missile guidance made possible by space technology held out the possibility of counterforce targeting so precise that an attack could leave its victim without the power to respond. Once again, superiority might have a meaning.

One extreme element of the anti-Communist coalition looked to spacewar as an escape from the restraints placed on military action by the power of nuclear weapons. Space is an infinitely large battlefield where innocent civilians are conveniently absent. After all, it was the horrible fear that millions would die that had prevented the Cold War from turning hot. For men whose lives have been dedicated to an ideal future where America prevails, the nuclear straitjacket preventing decisive military action is an encumbrance they'd like to remove. Space, the new high ground above the earth, offered the possibility of new weapons and new strategies unrestrained by the fear of nuclear holocaust. As General Bernard Schriever, former head of the Air Force Systems Command, once put it, "Of course I'd rather fight my wars in space and win them there than down here on our little planet." Space hawk generals found ready allies among America's aerospace corporations. The opening of a new environment to active military use would create the biggest potential new market for the aerospace corporations in decades. If the American people could be convinced or forced to pay for it, the new arms race would open a gold mine for the aerospace and weapons industries and their financiers.

Secretary Brown was not in the position to cancel the development of new space weapons the way McNamara did in the 1960s. Despite his own cogent analysis of the dangers of a space arms race, his and Carter's nuclear weapons policy called forth a new generation of highly accurate missiles—the MX, Cruise, Pershing II, and Trident—dependent on satellites for their pinpoint guidance accuracy. The development of powerful counterforce weapons led inexorably to demands for an operational ASAT system. For if the new generation of nuclear weapons was intended for a counterforce first strike against the Soviet nuclear forces (as their critics claimed and their supporters denied), then such a strike would require an ASAT attack against Soviet warning satellites, as well as their satellite communications links with their retaliatory forces. If instead, the counterforce weapons were intended to increase the number of nuclear options by limiting damage to chosen targets, in other words to improve the capability of fighting and winning a limited nuclear war, as the Carter National Security Directive #59 implied, then ASAT weapons would be targeted against the Soviets' most important satellites—their ocean surveillance spacecraft—as well as their ASAT interceptors.

Unless Harold Brown retreated from counterforce and limited nuclear war doctrine, his own arguments against arms in space would be undermined. Recognizing this, Brown did not cancel or even delay the air-launched ASAT project begun at the end of the Ford administration. Instead, he decided to pursue the advanced ASAT as a bargaining chip in negotiations with the Soviets on ASAT limitations.

At the opening of ASAT limitation talks, the U.S. objectives—first, to declare a bilateral prohibition against peacetime attacks against satellites and, second, to limit the development and deployment of ASATs to low-altitude orbits—appear to have been deliberately unambitious. The first objective would have done nothing to prevent or stall ASAT testing or deployment. The second, in the absence of a ban on weapons in space, would have been unfair to the Soviets, whose satellites in general fly at lower altitudes than do America's.

The Soviets took an equally unrealistic position, arguing for a ban on ASAT weapons and including the American space shuttle in their definition of an ASAT. Although it is true that the shuttle's capability to maneuver, rendezvous with, and even pluck satellites out of orbit could make it an acceptable ASAT, the shuttle's enormous cost and vulnerability to attack make it a very unlikely space warship.

Given the Soviet and American bargaining positions, the talks were doomed even before the events of 1979—the Iranian hostage crisis and the Soviet invasion of Afghanistan—hastened the return of the Cold War. As part of the American response to Soviet actions in Afghanistan, ASAT limitations talks were jettisoned. As of this writing they have not resumed. Work proceeded on the air-launched American ASAT, with testing scheduled to begin in 1982 or early 1983. (This schedule has not been met. At this writing the tests have not occurred, though they might at any time.) The Soviets renewed their ASAT test program, suspended during the talks. Eventually, they tested their ASAT system during global war games involving their entire strategic forces.

Carter's official emphasis on counterforce targeting and limited nuclear war strategy not only increased the importance of ASATs, but it opened up the whole question of satellite survivability in the event of war. When Harold Brown was director of Defense Research and Engineering in 1965, he had named as his number-one priority for the military space program in the post-Apollo period the achievement of satellite electronics protected from the effects of nuclear explosions. His second and third priorities in 1965 were the achievement of a reusable launch capability and an accurate navigation system for all the forces. By 1978, his lesser priorities were nearing achievement with the space shuttle and NAVSTAR. But between the time he left the Pentagon in 1969 and his return in 1977, satellite survivability had in general decreased, due to the ever-increasing complexity of the average satellite's design. With the United States preparing to fight and win nuclear wars that might last weeks or months, and with the likelihood that such wars would involve nuclear explosions in space, "hardening" against nuclear effects, in addition to "hardening" against nonnuclear ASAT attacks and protection against electromagnetic jamming, became particularly important to military space strategists.

The reliance on electronic C^3I has produced a burgeoning industry in the products of electronic warfare. Every time some new threat to the C^3I system, some new electronic countermeasure, is discovered, the military requires the overhaul of the entire network to make it invulnerable to the new discovery. The complex design requirements inevitably lead to confusion, complications, cost increases, and delays. As electronics development accelerates, delays can lead to a system becoming obsolete before it is even operational. The electronic arms race spins in a cycle of offensive measure conjuring forth defensive counter-measure leading to its countercountermeasure. More and more of the national wealth is squandered in this fashion. Some electronic warfare experts have suggested that if all-out war should ever occur, so many electromagnetic systems would be turned on at once that receivers everywhere would pick up nothing but noise.

The electronic arms race spiraling between the conflicting demands of improved real-time performance and satellite survivability accelerated during the Carter presidency. Between that and the costs of developing the MX, Cruise, Pershing, and Trident missiles, by late 1978 the administration was moving toward a total militarization of the economy. The government was forced to cut spending for social services in the face of a declining economy. Record federal deficits were caused in large part by escalating military expenses. With rapidly increased spending by both the Pentagon and the intelligence agencies on satellite technology and space systems, by 1978 the NASA budget was but a small percentage of total U.S. expenditures in space. With the NASA budget going almost exclusively to the space shuttle, a vehicle with a mostly military future, by 1978 U.S. space activity had been almost entirely militarized. The federal deficits, cuts in social services, declining civilian role in space, and astronomical defense spending that came later to define the Reagan presidency were well established in Carter's last two years in office.

Even as technology was becoming more complex and sophisticated, dramatic failures marked a universal low point for space activity in the late 1970s. On January 24, 1978, a Soviet spy satellite carrying a nuclear reactor and approximately one hundred pounds of Uranium-235 crashed into the northern Canadian wilderness, contaminating a large area. At a time of growing concern over nuclear reactors on earth, the public was suddenly made aware of the existence of satellites carrying reactors over their heads. The crash was the worst space-related nuclear accident since 1970, when the lunar lander of the aborted Apollo 13 mission, jettisoned upon reentry, carried its nuclear battery with over eight pounds of plutonium into the Pacific somewhere northwest of New Zealand.

In the aftermath of the Soviet spy satellite crash, President Carter publicly suggested a ban on nuclear reactors in space. But the president was quickly corrected by his military advisers. The new generation of

U.S. military satellites designed to withstand ASAT attack and the effects of nuclear explosions would be powered by nuclear batteries rather than vulnerable solar panels. Projected battle stations of the future might be powered by nuclear reactors. The Pentagon's plans for the accelerated militarization of space would be undermined by any ban on nuclear power. The president dropped his call for a ban, and the issue was soon forgotten. But the crash in the Canadian wilderness did manage momentarily to highlight the connection between space militarization and nuclear power in orbit. It suggested a future tactic for peace activists. Creating a public demand for a ban on nuclear power in orbit could be a successful organizing tool against future military activities in space.

Only a year after the crash of the Soviet Cosmos 954, the United States' abandoned Skylab space station began losing altitude, threatening to crash. Plans were made to send the new space shuttle up to Skylab to install booster rockets to carry it into higher, safer orbit. But slippage in the shuttle test schedule and acceleration of Skylab's orbital decay meant that nothing could be done to prevent an uncontrolled reentry. The world watched and waited to see where it would land. The sight of NASA engineers with all their techno-wizardry helpless to prevent their 130,000-pound spacecraft from falling back to earth further eroded public confidence in the experts' abilities to control what was going on above everyone's head.

In addition to doubts about technological abilities, the 1970s saw a growing suspicion about the potential totalitarian uses to which the new technology would be put. In the aftermath of Watergate, widespread *domestic* spying by U.S. intelligence agencies was revealed. The knowledge that those same intelligence agencies owned spy satellites capable of recording telephone conversations and cameras capable of picking individuals out of crowds and license plates out of highway traffic was met with what can only be called justified paranoia. In July 1978, the *New York Times* reported that the Central Intelligence Agency had used satellites in their surveillance campaign against Vietnam war dissidents.

A combination of factors—economic decline, loss of political support, distrust of technological solutions to social and political problems, concern for the environment, dramatic space accidents, and fear of the connections between America's space program and its nuclear war-making schemes—combined to create a space picture very different from what the futurists of the 1950s and 1960s had believed probable in the seventies and eighties. It took less than ten years from John Kennedy's commitment to a lunar landing for American astronauts to land on the moon. Predictions about the future made then, based upon the generally accepted dogma of accelerating technological progress, held that ten years after that, by 1980, space flight would be almost routine. Speaking in the Philippines shortly after the first moon landing, Richard Nixon had promised President Ferdinand Marcos that Marcos's son would fly aboard the first commercial transporter to the moon. Pan American and Trans World Airlines had offered to take reservations for the first commercial moonflights. NASA's associate administrator, George Mueller, had predicted that space stations in earth orbit would hold 150 people, including tourists, and that another station circling the moon would hold twenty-five more. Wernher von Braun, placed in charge of NASA's future planning in 1970, had expected astronauts to land on Mars in the 1980s and suggested that the president fly aboard the shuttle to NASA's space station for the nation's bicentennial celebration in 1976. No one had predicted that the late 1970s would see a space station fall uncontrollably out of the skies, a shuttle delayed by years, and the future of space exploration and life on the home planet compromised by satellites' incorporation into the holocaust fantasies of nuclear war planners.

It is worthwhile to remember the huge gap between reality and the predictions made about space activities by the futurists of the 1960s. In the 1980s, futurists promise space colonies, factories, and exotic new space weapons for the 1990s and the next century. Although most of the current batch of futurists' visions are as unlikely as Nixon's, Mueller's, or Von Braun's were in their time, it won't prevent deluded futurists and spacehawk generals from squandering countless billions of dollars pursuing their goals.

Whether it's the energy corporations hyping solar-power transmission via satellite, right-wing think tanks praising the glories of space-based laser weapons, or science fictionists imagining orbiting utopias, they all bank their future on the U.S. space shuttle's ability to open space to routine use. The shuttle's mixed performance in its early years shows the strain of having to carry the burden of so many conflicting visions into the future.

15

The Space Shuttle

The space shuttle is one of the most imaginative inventions in the history of political compromise. It was promoted as a neutral concept, a transportation system, so nobody was forced to say what would be transported by whom to where. The U.S. space program planners were in such a quandary about what to do and where to go after the moon that the shuttle seemed like the perfect vehicle. For NASA, it offered a means to stay in the manned space flight business through the post-Apollo drought. To the aerospace industry, it was a major new batch of contracts and a consolation for the loss of government funding for the projected supersonic transport plane (SST) that Congress had rejected in the same session that approved the shuttle. To the Air Force, it was a consolation for the canceled MOL space station and something close to the Dyna-Soar the Systems Command under General Schriever had been clamoring for for years. To congressional critics of the high costs of space activity, it promised reduced costs in the future.

The only real objection to the shuttle came from scientists connected to NASA itself, who feared that the engineers had taken over the agency and that henceforth vehicle design and excessive futurism would dominate over scientifically valuable programs. Money for planetary exploration had been cut in the same Nixon budget that began shuttle development work. George Rathjens, a space scientist at M.I.T., commenting on the sales pitch NASA and the Air Force had presented, told a congressional committee that they had received a "snow job" or a "hard sell." [1] But despite the dramatic successes of the Pioneer and Viking planetary probes, planetary scientists had only a tiny constituency compared to the industry and military, who had their sights on big-budget programs for near-earth space.

Certainly there was nothing new in the idea of reusability. Any observer of the early NASA programs had to wonder about multi-million-dollar vehicles being used once and then tossed away. But while spacecraft reusability might be a simple idea, it presented extremely difficult design problems. Materials would have to withstand the grueling pressures of launch, the extremes of temperature in space, and the scorching friction heat of reentry—not once but repeatedly. Materials for and design and construction of a reusable vehicle would be considerably more expensive than for throwaway vehicles. And vehicle costs were but a fraction of the total costs of a mission also involving ground equipment, launch facilities, fuel, and so forth. So although reusability ultimately suggested savings, those savings would only be realized over time and after launches had become frequent.

The dilemma presented by reusability was stated clearly by General Schriever in 1967. As he pointed out, "We can't actually justify the high costs of developing reusable systems until we have the necessary volume of space missions; at the same time we can't cost-effectively program any high utilization of space vehicles until the cost comes down." Of course, Schriever had no difficulty naming the missions he would like to see fill up the necessary volume for a reusable system. He liked to speak of the six R's of military space operations: "rendezvous, resupply, repair, replace, rescue, and return." [2]

The Air Force Dyna-Soar had been promoted as a reusable transportation vehicle in much the same fashion as the later space shuttle. In reports prepared by the Air Force in the early 1960s, Dyna-Soar was touted as a "routine space transporter" whose "reusability will contribute greatly to economical, routine space operations." [3] The "Dyna-Soar can also provide the means for in-orbit repair, maintenance and recovery of the hardware." [4]

During the intense intergovernmental debates in the mid-sixties over what space programs should follow the moon landing, General Schriever named a reusable transportation system as a higher priority for the Air Force than even antisatellite weapons or the manned orbiting laboratory. He retired from his post at the Air Force Systems Command partly in protest over the Johnson administration's lack of support for developing reusable space systems. Under Schriever, the Air Force Systems Command continuously maintained that military and civilian spacecraft involved totally different requirements. But in 1968, after ten years of research and development, the Dyna-Soar program was officially canceled. By 1970, the Air Force had faced fiscal and political reality and agreed to join with NASA in developing the shuttle.

Clearly, in the post-Apollo political environment, NASA could not have projected the necessary volume of space missions to justify the high costs of developing a reusable system alone. With NASA's ambitious post-Apollo plans for large, permanently occupied space stations and journeys to Mars on hold, NASA administrators looked for a new rationale for a major space vehicle project to follow the moon landing. NASA took their space shuttle design (which had been just one component of an earth-to-space transportation system that included a space station in low earth orbit and an earth-to-moon shuttle) to the Air Force and offered a bargain. In exchange for a commitment to redesign its satellites to fit into shuttle-launch configurations and a promise to use the shuttle exclusively in the future, NASA would accept Air Force design changes needed to increase the payload capacity and allow take-off and landing from Vandenburg Air Force Base.

The redesigned shuttle orbiter and its cargo bay would now be able to launch large single satellites, many small ones, or a number of different experiments at once. The Air Force also insisted on having the capability to return to launch site after one polar orbit. As a spacecraft circles the earth once on a polar orbit at an altitude of 250 miles, the earth turns roughly 1100 miles beneath it. Therefore, if the shuttle were to take off and complete only one polar orbit, it would reenter 1100 miles to the west of its launch site. In order to return to launch site for landing—necessary for a quick single-orbit reconnaissance flight or a sudden abort of a sensitive military mission—it would have to glide those 1100 miles laterally during reentry and descent, increasing the atmospheric friction, placing greater stress on the frame and its heat shielding, in other words, complicating the design demands.

In addition to design changes, Air Force use of the shuttle would require a second launch facility on the West Coast in addition to using NASA's facilities at Cape Canaveral. The shuttle could not be sent into polar orbit from Florida since the launch trajectory would carry it over the heavily populated eastern seaboard during ascent, when it would jettison its external fuel tank. Polar orbiting satellites are launched from Vandenburg Air Force Base in Lompoc, California. Facilities there would be upgraded to accommodate the shuttle.

The additional Air Force design requirements and the need for a second launch site greatly increased the projected cost of the shuttle program; but they also guaranteed that when NASA went before Congress for its yearly appropriations, it would have the powerful political backing of the Air Force and the Defense Department.

By 1972 the Space Transportation System was a joint NASA/Defense Department project. The schedule called for flight tests in the atmosphere in 1975 and 1976, with the first space flight in 1978 and operational status achieved by 1980. Each shuttle orbiter was estimated to cost $250 million. (In 1983, the estimated cost of an orbiter had grown to $1 billion.) Seven shuttle orbiters were projected to fly 725 missions over the course of their lifetimes. (At this writing, two orbiters have flown, two are under construction, and debate rages over the need for a fifth orbiter.)

The Air Force was assigned the task of developing an upper-stage rocket to carry shuttle payloads from the low-earth orbit flown by the orbiter out to higher orbits—geostationary and beyond. Some kind of high energy upper stage is essential for the military use of the shuttle. Many of the military's largest and most complex satellites are meant to fly in stationary orbits. To meet the need, the Air Force proposed the design for an Inertial Upper Stage (IUS). (The name was later changed to Interim Upper Stage when the IUS began running into difficulties and a simpler, less powerful rocket was adopted for the interim until a workable, affordable high-energy upper stage could be invented.) Originally, each flight of the IUS was projected to cost $5 million. Cost projections for lifting large platforms into geostationary orbit with the IUS in the mid-1980s now stand at $125 million each. As the price of upper stage has increased, potential customers have gone to other launch means. For this reason, two of the major Air Force satellites once scheduled for IUS launch, the NAVSTAR and Satellite Data System spacecraft, have abandoned it. Growing doubts about the Space Transportation System's military usefulness and economic viability have resulted.

In 1976, when the Air Force and NASA joined to identify missions suitable for the shuttle, they discovered that most of them involved subsequent developments beyond the shuttle itself—e.g., in-space assembly of large structures; space tugs for transportation from orbit to orbit; energy supplies of greater power and reliability; permanently manned space stations and work platforms.[5] The technologies and skills required by these further developments were little understood, and their eventual costs unpredictable. Spending $20 billion to develop a space shuttle threatened to become little more than an outrageously expensive research and development project unless it got all its accompanying spaceware.

Schriever's dilemma remains. You can't justify spending billions to build the rest of the transportation system until you have something you intend to do with it. But you can't spend billions developing the skills, materials, and programs for projects in space without viable transportation. The alternatives are limited. America can abandon the shuttle and accept the loss of money, time, and prestige involved. America can fund it as a research and development project. Or America can commit itself to a major expansion of capabilities. NASA and the military clearly intended to make the third choice. According to the 1976 joint NASA–Air Force study on shuttle utilization, "While full advantage is taken of the Space Shuttle's multiple payload capability, only limited advantage is taken of the other unique capabilities offered by the reusable transportation system. Therefore it is expected that broad new national defense concepts and programs will evolve to exploit the Space Transportation's capability and gain significant military benefits during the 1983–1991 time period and beyond."[6] As NASA administrator in charge of the shuttle program and former Air Force Secretary Hans Mark put it, "The Space Shuttle is important with a capital 'I'. It was just thirty years ago that we set up an Air Force. That was a new technology that required a new service. Something similar will happen with the Shuttle."[7]

NASA administrator James Beggs told a House subcommittee in August 1982, "It makes sense to make [the shuttle] the primary vehicle because, since it is an expensive vehicle from the point of view of putting in the infrastructure, the things to make it work, the more you can fly it the lower the cost for any individual flight, so it makes sense to make it the overall vehicle."[8]

Regardless of military intentions, the structure and ideology of American government causes administrations to shy away from huge civilian projects. In the 1980s, the question of how to organize America's space program in the shuttle era has not been determined. Some have suggested that, in the future, the shuttle be operated like the railroads, as a commercial venture. But even if the military were willing to allow their future space ambitions to rest on the whims of profit, there would still be no private financial institutions willing to invest such huge amounts on futuristic projects whose returns would not be seen, if ever, for decades. NASA is, by law, forbidden to run an operational commercial venture. If a government corporation were to be set up to finance the venture into space, it would run head-on into America's antisocialist traditions. It seems likely that, despite years of holding it up before the international community as an example of America's peaceful global intentions, the space program will finally openly become the military program it has always largely been anyway. As a Georgetown University space researcher and author Michel Michaud told the Fourth Princeton Conference on Space Manufacturing, "The Department of Defense not only spends more on R & D than any other institution in America—it is also freer to work on riskier projects, whose cost benefit may be very uncertain. . . . It was R & D for military aircraft that made possible the jet airliners we know today. . . . It may be that only military requirements will allow us to breach the cost barrier and to take space policy out of the hands of the Office of Management and Budget." [9]

The great danger is that the political economy of space activity encourages some, who might not otherwise, to support the grandiose schemes of the spacehawk generals. The coalition that gathered around the shuttle program at its inception—NASA, the industry, space buffs, and those with a genuine emotional attachment to the dreams of space flight—is pressured, perhaps against its members' better judgment, to acquiesce to, and even to invite, the accelerated militarization of space. The future of the shuttle almost certainly depends on the military thinking up more and better things to do with it. Almost as sure, given the history of military ingenuity, the things they think up to do will place the planet in greater and greater peril.

The shuttle, NAVSTAR, and advanced military communications systems all approached operation in the late 1970s, and the costs of military space programs expanded accordingly. Between 1975 and 1980, funding for the Air Force Space and Missile Systems Organization doubled. By 1979 it had grown so large that it was split in two, forming the Air Force Space Division and the Ballistic Missile Office.

By 1980 the technological momentum of the military was almost unstoppable. A decision had to be made about America's—and the world's—future in space. The shuttle was the key element. If the United States were to commit itself to a modest military space program based on treaty verification, early warning, communications and weather satellites, or if it were to move toward international cooperation and peacekeeping, then expendable launch vehicles would be more economical; the shuttle could be maintained for scientific and engineering research. But if the United States were to commit itself to the military control of space with armed battle stations, spaceplanes, and giant surveillance systems, then it would need the capabilities the shuttle offered.

A public policy debate should have been held in 1980, before the first shuttle flew. As it was, in the absence of debate and coordinated decision making, the technological momentum established pushed the nation's military toward greater levels of space activity.

16

The Space Warriors Return

The election of Ronald Reagan signaled the end of U.S. efforts even to pretend that American space activities would be dedicated to peaceful purposes. The most extreme space militarists, having attached themselves to Reagan's rising star, would now have free rein in the formulation of U.S. space policy. Reagan's military adviser in the election campaign, Retired General Daniel O. Graham, was the former head of the Defense Intelligence Agency and an outspoken supporter of space-based missile defense systems. After the election, Reagan appointed a transition team to advise him on space and science policy. Two of the team's members, Edward Teller and Retired General Bernard Schriever, had for thirty years been encouraging America to seize the "high ground" through military superiority in space.

Teller, the "father of the hydrogen bomb," had been crucial in establishing in the mid-fifties that H-bombs could be made small enough to fit in the nose cone of Schriever's ICBMs. He had also testified before Congress in favor of building a military base on the moon. He had been a vigorous opponent of every arms control agreement ever signed between the United States and the USSR, including the 1963 Test Ban Treaty and the 1967 Outer Space Treaty, which had banned nuclear weapons from earth orbit. Along with Schriever, Teller served on the 1960 panel that recommended future Air Force space activities. The panel's recommendations were for the development of the Dyna-Soar as an aerospace bomber, antisatellite weapons, a manned military space station, a reusable shuttle, and a space-based ABM system. Teller had a particular interest in the effects of thermonuclear weapons and had a long-standing concern about the survivability of the nation's military communications in the event of war. He had supported the Air Force's manned space station, Project MOL, as a demonstration of the potential for a space-based command center for controlling nuclear forces. Among his more recent pet projects was demonstrating the feasibility of basing high-energy lasers in space as part of a global missile defense system.

157

Along with General Schriever and Teller, other members of Reagan's science policy transition team included Simon Ramo of TRW, Inc.; Arthur Bueche, General Electric's vice-president for corporate research; and Edward David, head of research for Exxon and former science adviser to President Nixon. The transition report on space was written by General Schriever.

Schriever, in helping to formulate the new administration's space policy, reaffirmed the radical militarist position, which had over the years brought him into conflict with previous administrations. Even before Sputnik, Schriever was publicly proclaiming that space would be the battleground of the future. In 1957, the Pentagon, worried about the budgetary repercussions if Schriever's ideas ever became politically popular, expressly forbade him to mention the word *space* in his public speeches.

Schriever never understood why Congress had passed the NASA act, which had committed the nation to pursuing peaceful, scientific activities in space. According to Schriever, the NASA act "completely misled the American people as to the potential use of space for national security." [1] All the NASA act did according to Schriever was make it difficult to justify military space programs to the Congress and American people. He blamed the difficulties he had faced in his thirty years of working for the militarization of space on popular misconceptions about the purposes of space activity. In Schriever's own colorful language, "Space for peaceful purposes—what a bunch of goddamned bullshit that was!"

Schriever's quest for military superiority in space is a quest for *absolute* superiority, unchallengable power. "What I want is a radar surveillance system which allows you to spot everything that's moving, either on the surface or above the surface of the earth. And if we had a number of companion systems, a high-energy laser, or particle beam weapon, or something else along with the pointing and tracking ability to knock down airplanes and missiles, then you wouldn't even need to knock out cities; you could knock out forces. You could pin your enemy down on earth. What would they do? If I control the high ground and you can't move, what are you going to do? You're going to negotiate a surrender. That's what it's all about."

The Defense Advanced Research Projects Agency (DARPA) plans to launch a surveillance system not unlike what Schriever described. The

Advanced Sensor Demonstration is scheduled for launch from the space shuttle in 1988. It will go into geostationary orbit, from where it will detect and track airplanes as well as missiles. A number of ocean surveillance systems for tracking surface ships and submarines are also underway. The accompanying pointing and tracking techniques for space lasers or particle beam weapons are also being developed under various Defense research projects.

To Schriever, the rationale for total control from space is clear. "The Soviets are our enemies. As long as we stay strong, no matter what it takes, I think we have a chance of prevailing in the world. Because our form of government and communism will not be forever apart. One side or the other is going to prevail."

To object to his ideas is to be guilty of some muddleheaded concern about contaminating space. "We talk about saving a fish here, and something else there, the environmental thing, and so there seems to be this objection, 'let's keep space clean.' But there isn't much we can do to make space dirty. One star exploding in the universe is going to contaminate space more than all the nuclear bombs we could ever use. There's no reason to say 'space for peaceful purposes.' We'd all be better off with our wars in space rather than on land."

But despite his claims that war in space would be better for humanity, he admits that such wars would "finally end up on land anyway; that's where the final decision will be made." Space weapons are being created to *participate* in war on earth, *not* to replace it.

With Schriever's ideas guiding the formulation of Reagan's space policy, the trend toward unrestrained militarization, already apparent in the final years of the Carter presidency, became doctrine. On October 2, 1981, the Reagan administration announced its five-part program to improve America's nuclear war–fighting capability: (1) one hundred B-1 bombers to be deployed by 1986, while research continues on advanced intercontinental bombers and stealth bombers for the 1990s; (2) one hundred MX missiles, with type of deployment to be decided later; (3) development of a Trident II missile with a 6500-mile range; (4) improvement of the C^3I network so that it can survive all types of nuclear war; and (5) improvement of defenses by upgrading radar systems, initiating a broad program of civil defense, and increasing research and development of antiballistic missile systems. In addition, Reagan's five-point strategic military space program was unveiled: (1) improvement of the survivability of ground-receiving and data-processing stations to ensure access to satellite data during a nuclear war; (2) improvement of the warning satellites; (3) development of a new satellite communications system using Extreme High Frequency channels to ensure two-way communications and control over strategic forces in an extended nuclear conflict; (4) creation of an operational ASAT system; and (5) research and development on a space-based missile-defense system.

Perhaps the most concise statement of the Reagan administration's military planning is contained in a document written by Defense Secretary Caspar Weinberger titled "Fiscal Year 1984–1988 Defense Guidance." The document was obtained by the *New York Times*, which published excerpts from it in May 1983. The document states that the United States should develop weapons that "are difficult for the Soviets to counter, impose disproportionate costs, *open up new areas of major military competition*, and obsolesce previous Soviet investments." For fighting future nonnuclear wars "it will be necessary to move generally toward a mix of forces that includes more widely distributed and mobile forces capable of protecting controlled, long range and precise firepower. The goal for our forces in the future should guide our research and development as well as our procurement efforts." The document placed special emphasis on strategic communications, saying they "must provide the capability to execute ad hoc plans, even subsequent to repeated attacks. In particular, these systems should support the reconstitution and execution of strategic reserve forces, specifically full communication with our strategic nuclear submarines." [2]

From the beginning of the Reagan presidency, space programs multiplied to meet these requirements: force mobility, precise long-range firepower, and protracted nuclear war fighting. A major contradiction existed between nuclear doctrine, which called for the capability to prevail in an extended nuclear war, and the C^3I network coordinating the forces, which probably would shut down in the hostile environment of nuclear war. Therefore, top priority went to upgrading communications survivability in order to make them compatible with the nuclear doctrine. According to the official statement of Air Force policy, presented to the Senate Armed Services Committee by Secretary of the Air Force Verne Orr and Chief of Staff General Lew Allen, "Perhaps no portion of our strategic modernization program is as important as upgrading C^3 systems. Technology has enabled us to gain better understanding of the disruptive effects of nuclear weapons on our command and control communications systems. Our present landline, radio and satellite systems could be seriously disrupted during trans- and post-nuclear attack." In order to meet this challenge, the Air Force is "exploring improved satellite capabilities at frequency ranges which can sustain communications in a jamming environment and a nuclear disturbed atmosphere."[3]

Secretary Weinberger told the committee, "The Reagan administration has given the highest priority to increasing the ability of our strategic-force management systems not only to survive, but to remain capable of performing their basic functions throughout a sustained sequence of Soviet attacks."[4]

Shortly after assuming duties as the new undersecretary of Defense for Research and Engineering, Richard DeLauer brought together representatives of the armed services and the intelligence agencies to plan a new national system of global communications to serve all top-priority military users. Robert Cooper, the director of DARPA, defined the new system's requirements: "We must provide for the threat that may exist in a nuclear conflict and provide for the survivability of those few space systems that would be needed to support the national command authorities in their actions during the short period of time at the beginning of the war, and then provide for enduring capability to manage the recovery of the country from such a potential conflict."[5]

In wartime, satellites could face three distinct threats: ASAT attack, the effects of nuclear explosions in space, and electromagnetic jamming of its signals and other disruptive electronic measures against itself and its ground elements. It is one task to ensure satellite survivability for the brief moments required for a one-time nuclear retaliation in response to a Soviet nuclear attack; it is another task altogether to develop systems that can survive all levels of conflict, including an extended period of nuclear warfare.

The techniques of survivability can be summed up as: camouflage, mobility, proliferation, active defense, hardening, and replacement. It may not be that difficult to design a spacecraft to endure any particular offensive measure, but to design it to withstand all imaginable threats is probably impossible. Research often concentrates on one threat while ignoring glaring vulnerabilities in other parts of the system. For example, while efforts to make a satellite jamproof and survivable are undertaken, the ground equipment to receive the satellite's messages remain highly vulnerable. Even the Aerospace Command Center buried beneath Cheyenne Mountain and protected from every conceivable form of attack receives communications via microwave towers that are vulnerable to blast and radiation effects. The problem may be insurmountable. The more complex the electronics and data processing aboard a satellite are, the more vulnerable the satellite is to nuclear effects. If the satellite is kept simple, then sensitive receivers and information processing must be placed on the ground. If the ground equipment is to be simple and dependable, then the satellite must have a powerful transmitter and on-board processing and be vulnerable as a result.

Work on communications survivability techniques has been ongoing for better than a decade. On March 14, 1976, two spacecraft were launched to test advanced communications techniques. Built by the Lincoln Laboratory at the Massachusetts Institute of Technology, the satellites were named Lincoln Experimental Satellite (LES) 8 and 9. Crucial circuits were shielded and hardened against the effects of nuclear explosions. The satellite was driven by on-board plutonium batteries rather than vulnerable solar panels and used Extreme High Frequency communication beams, on-board data-processing and anti-jam techniques. The techniques first tested by LES 8 and 9 were incorporated into the third-generation Defense Satellite Communication System (DSCS 3). In 1980, a model of the DSCS 3 was tested while being exposed to a nuclear blast in an underground vault in Nevada. According to reports of the test, it gave confidence that the satellite would survive in a radiation enhanced environment such as would exist in space during and after a nuclear war. The first of the operational DSCS 3 spacecraft was placed in geostationary orbit in October 1982.

The DSCS is designed for the long haul communications to the principal command centers around the world. It is but one segment of a communications network known as MILSTAR. According to the Department of Defense 1983 posture statement, "MILSTAR satellite communication system is designed to provide survivable and enduring C^3 for decision makers who must be able to direct and receive information from forces through all levels of conflict, including general nuclear war." [6] The heart of the system will consist of eight MILSTAR satellites, five in geostationary and three in polar orbits. The ground segment will consist of terminals aboard aircraft, ships, submarines, jeeps, armored track vehicles, and fixed terrestrial sites. In addition to the dedicated

MILSTAR satellites and the DSCS spacecraft, the remainder of the MILSTAR system consists of the Navy's FLTSATCOM satellites; the Satellite Data System (SDS), which among other tasks relays real-time surveillance information to intelligence headquarters from the Keyhole (KH 11) spy satellites; and NASA's Tracking and Data Relay Satellites (TDRS), which will keep track of other spacecraft and relay information across space, back to ground stations in the United States, thus eliminating America's politically sensitive dependence on foreign ground-tracking and data-reception stations.

One of the most difficult communications tasks is to maintain contact with the nation's ballistic missile submarine fleet. Currently, strategic submarines are incapable of receiving Emergency Action Messages directly from the FLTSATCOM system, which are transmitted at frequencies that cannot penetrate ocean water. A fleet of EC-130A aircraft continuously roam the seas to relay messages it receives on UHF and EHF channels to the submarines via Very Low Frequency signals, which can penetrate ten to fifteen meters. The submarines keep a long antenna wire riding near the surface with which it transmits and receives messages. The whole process facilitates Soviet efforts to track America's submarines.

Theoretically, laser communications using blue-green laser light could penetrate the ocean depths. A number of research projects are underway to develop blue-green laser communications to complement the MILSTAR system.

Improvements in strategic communications were made necessary by the Reagan administration's insistence that "these systems should support the reconstitution and execution of strategic reserve forces" during a "protracted conflict period."[7] The Reagan administration has requested nearly $20 billion over the five-year strategic program for the improvement of communications systems.

Similarly, the Reagan administration's plan to field "a mix of forces that includes more widely distributed and mobile forces capable of protecting controlled, long-range and precise firepower"[8] necessitates continued development and improvement of the NAVSTAR Global Positioning System, which is now scheduled to be completely operational in the late 1980s. By the year 2000, there may be as many as 20,000 NAVSTAR receiver units aboard all manner of military vehicles and ballistic and cruise missiles.

By 1983, six NAVSTAR satellites were in orbit. Eighteen working satellites and three spares will be required before the system is completely operational. Later satellites will include several features required by new nuclear war–fighting strategies: hardening against nuclear effects, signal processing to make it available only to selected receivers, and design adjustments allowing it to carry the new IONDS nuclear-blast detectors.

The Integrated Operational Nuclear Detection System (IONDS) is designed exclusively for protracted nuclear war. Richard DeLauer, the Pentagon's director of research, explains: "IONDS will be capable of detecting, locating, and reporting, in near real-time, nuclear detonations on a global basis. IONDS will provide strike and damage assessment information, thereby enhancing strategic force management."[9] In other words, during a nuclear war distant commanders in their "hardened" shelters will be able to watch global thermonuclear war unfold before them on their video display terminals. According to how many warheads successfully detonate at any given target, decisions will be made concerning subsequent strikes throughout the protracted conflict.

The very existence of IONDS highlights a disturbing fact of the Space Age: advances in space technology have given military leaders the impression that the awesome power of nuclear weapons can be "managed" and directed toward the achievement of rational strategic goals. It is as if space flight has engendered a widespread delusion of grandeur. The fantasy that lies behind the satellite technology for nuclear war management is that somehow, from space, nuclear war will be neater and less horrifying—and under control.

Given the Reagan administration's efforts to integrate satellites into operational weapons systems and its decision to "open up new areas of military competition" with the Soviets, it is not surprising that it has also encouraged the development of new space weapons and accelerated the schedule for deploying America's air-launched ASAT weapons. At the same time, the administration refused to reopen ASAT limitation negotiations. In 1982, the Soviets proposed to the United Nations General Assembly that it take up as an item on its agenda "the conclusion of a treaty banning the deployment of any weapons in outer space."[10] Difficulties do exist in negotiating such a treaty. In particular, the problem of establishing a clear and meaningful definition of the term *weapon* and the Soviets' past insistence on including the American shuttle in their definition. But clearly, no treaty can be concluded unless all parties show a willingness to talk, and the Reagan administration has steadfastly refused to consider a ban on space weapons. A resolution was introduced into Congress in 1982 and 1983 calling on the president to "begin immediate negotiations for a ban on weapons of any kind in space." As of this writing, the resolution has made little progress. (See Appendix 1.) A treaty banning weapons in space holds little appeal to a president convinced by his advisers that somewhere out in space lies the key to recapturing the superiority America's military once enjoyed.

No space-weapons scheme has received as much attention as the various proposals for a system of space-based antiballistic missiles to defend the U.S. against a Soviet nuclear attack. Ballistic missile defense from space is not a new idea. The Air Force worked on a project in the late 1950s and early 1960s known as BAMBI, for ballistic missile boost intercept. BAMBI would have consisted of hundreds of satellites armed with heat-seeking missiles that would be fired at Soviet ICBMs during their period of assent. BAMBI was canceled in 1963 because the McNamara Defense Department considered it unworkable.

The idea was revived and popularized in 1980 through the efforts of a well-known right-wing think tank, the Heritage Foundation. The foundation sponsored a study group named the High Frontier, Inc., which issued a grand design for the future of American efforts in space.[11] The ballistic missile defense system was only one of five major proposals. The others—a high-performance spaceplane, improved space transportation, a manned low-earth orbit space station, and a solar-power satellite in geostationary orbit—offered something to almost every part of the "prospace" constituency. But the most controversial was its proposal to place 432 missile carrying "trucks" into low-earth orbit, as the boost-phase segment of its three-tiered missile defense. According to the study's author, Retired General Daniel O. Graham, a former Reagan military adviser, the boost-phase defense could be constructed out of available technology. The trucks would each carry 30 to 150 guided interceptors using the same pointing, tracking, and guidance systems to be used by the air-launched ASAT system.

Those ICBMs that made it past the High Frontier's boost interceptors would next be confronted by a mid-course defense, probably based on satellites in geostationary orbit. General Graham admits that the sensors required to target postboost, "cool" ICBMs as they arc through space are well beyond available technology.

The final tier in the three-tier defense would consist of ground-based ABMs to defend America's Minuteman silos. Estimates of the cost of the High Frontier defense system range from $15 billion to an astonishing $1 *trillion*.

Initially, the Defense Department criticized the proposals for space ABMs. Richard DeLauer told Arms Control hearings in the Senate, "Two weaknesses, as far as I am concerned, are the time it would take and the amount of money that it would take; I think they are both grossly underestimated [by their supporters]." DARPA chief Robert Cooper added, "I think there could be one other reason added to Dr. DeLauer's other reason why it is unlikely that anyone could do that [space ABMs] in the near term. The enormous complexity of such a system is unmanageable today, in our judgment, and we need basic I would call them breakthroughs in the ability to manage large complex systems before any such system might be feasible in the future." [12] Reagan's own science advisers had become convinced that a space-based ABM system would be implausible.

But President Reagan surprised his own staff by publicly supporting the concept of space-based missile defense in his notorious "Star Wars" speech on March 18, 1983. Apparently, the president was convinced by his friend and adviser Edward Teller that a space ABM was not only plausible, but inevitable. The president called for a long-term research and development program. The administration requested $2.6 billion for space ABMs in Fiscal Year 1984 and $3.1 billion for 1985.

Edward Teller's space ABM proposal is considerably different than the one proposed by the High Frontier. Teller's is based on what he calls "third-generation" (the first being the atomic bomb; the second, the Hydrogen bomb) nuclear weapons, such as nuclear driven X-ray lasers that focus and concentrate the destructive power of a nuclear explosion into a directed energy beam. Such an X-ray laser, known as Excalibur, was tested at the Nevada underground site. Reports of the test conflict as to whether or not it was successful.

The Excalibur is just one of a large and growing list of directed energy weapons being suggested for use in space. Beam weapons all require three basic components: a destructive beam and something to power it; a way to aim and control the beam; and an "intelligence" to decide when to shoot at what. Each of these components has a host of technological difficulties standing in the way of deploying a workable system.

As part of the White House effort in this field, President Reagan issued National Security Study Directive 6-83. According to the *Aviation Week* report outlining the study directive, it "instructs the Pentagon to conduct studies with the following objectives: to assess the role that an effective ballistic missile defense could play in the security of the U.S.; to define a long-term research and development program aimed at an ultimate goal of eliminating the threat posed by nuclear ballistic missiles."[13]

The Defense Department has three major ongoing areas of space laser research, sometimes known as the space laser triad. Project Alpha is aimed at the basic technology issues of chemical lasers. Project LODE (large optics demonstration experiments) studies methods to control the beam. And Project Talon Gold is an experiment, scheduled to be flown aboard the shuttle, to test the advanced methods of target acquisition and precision aiming that would be required by a space laser.

Laser weapons research had become a minor political issue by the end of the Carter years. A group of influential Republicans led by Utah's Senator Jake Garn and Wyoming's Malcolm Wallop succeeded in adding $20 million to the president's budget request for laser weapons research. The amended budget item specified that the additional funds be spent on space ABM research. The following year the same group led the Senate to a vote approving $50 million to fund planning for an early in-orbit demonstration of laser weapons. A number of representatives from the aerospace industry, recognizing a potential mother lode of new contracts, joined together to lobby Congress for even greater support of space laser programs. The lobbying group, headed by Lockheed's Maxwell Hunter, included representatives from TRW, Inc., North American Rockwell, Bell Aerospace, and Perkin-Elmer (producers of laser mirrors).

Laser weapons have drawn perhaps the most popular attention in the current round of space militarization. Comic strip visions of silent, bloodless destruction, where cartoon-type enemies are zapped—neatly vaporized—explain much of the appeal of lasers, particle beams, and other directed energy weapons. Scientists discovered how to produce a laser beam in 1960. Two years later the Army, Navy, and Air Force each had its own laser weapons research program. Since then, both ground and airborne lasers have been successfully tested against a variety of targets.

Visible light energy is normally emitted randomly, spreading out in all directions equally. In 1960, physicists discovered a means to stimulate certain atoms to emit photons of light energy at the same frequency, and in phase with the stimulating photon. Using special mirrors, the resultant light can be amplified and focused, building light wave on light wave to create an intense beam. The power of the beam depends on the source of the stimulation.

Laser weapons appear to be well suited for use in space. Space provides the vacuum lasers require for the stimulation process and offers none of the difficulties associated with atmospheric scattering of the beam and subsequent loss of power. Traveling at 186,000 miles per second, the speed of light, a destructive beam can cover the vast distances to targets in space almost instantaneously, thus simplifying targeting and firing.

Though they appear ideal in the abstract realm of imagined combat scenarios, research on laser battle stations is vexed with a host of technological, political, and fiscal uncertainties. For instance, how can missile-defense systems avoid being obsolesced by new offensive countermeasures? Many such countermeasures come readily to mind. ICBMs could be coated with a special substance to reflect the beam harmlessly away. Thousands of decoys could be launched to exhaust the ABM's capacity. A space ABM capable of autonomous target acquisition, tracking and aiming, and autonomous decision making as to when to fire at what targets would require extremely complex artificial intelligence and highly refined and delicate sensors. These would necessarily be vulnerable to electronic countermeasures and, in particular, to the effects of nuclear explosions. Couldn't an enemy intent on launching an ICBM attack maneuver nuclear-armed satellites near to enough ABM battle stations to nullify the system's effectiveness? Even the most optimistic supporters of space ABMs estimate the time required to deploy operational battle stations as a decade or more. Plenty of time would be available to an enemy to invent simple countermeasures, and at far less expense than the billions needed for the ABM.

In order to cover every ballistic missile trajectory between the Soviet

Union and the United States, dozens, perhaps hundreds of laser battle stations would be required, with all their accompanying fuel and control elements. Each one would be more complex than anything yet sent into orbit. Each would need accompanying defense against all kinds of imaginable ASAT attacks. As the Pentagon's Defense Science Board noted in its 1981 report on space lasers, "Offensive and defensive weapons always work together, and in this case adversaries—unwilling to live without an offensive capability—would undoubtedly plan to attack space lasers with ASAT systems, including other space lasers, so as to free their offensive forces." [14] An incredibly massive space arms race would result.

Lasers need fuel; the more powerful they are the more fuel they need. Some estimates of the requirements range as high as two million pounds of fuel for each chemical laser battle station in orbit. The X-ray laser would theoretically eliminate the problem of bulk by deriving its power from low-yield nuclear devices. But it would raise its own set of problems, including the international political outrage sure to greet a plan to encircle the planet with nuclear bombs.

Even if, by a stroke of luck or technical genius, all the uncertainties were eliminated and all the ballistic missile routes now open to the Soviet Union were effectively policed by laser sentries in space, what would happen if another enemy nation—Libya? Iran? China?—built its own ICBM force? (With the United States boldly adding space laser weapons to its arsenal, is there any hope that nuclear weapons and ICBMs would not proliferate?) Would the United States then need more and more space ABMs targeted on all corners of the globe? And even if the earth was successfully rid of ICBMs forever, the same force of technology that created the space lasers would lead to alternative means of mass destruction. ICBMs are not the only bombardment system; just the only ones vulnerable to space-based defense. Cruise missiles, low-flying bombers, and short-range submarine-launched missiles would all be unaffected. And nuclear weapons are not the only means of mass annihilation. Other environmental, biological, psychological, or chemical weapons could easily be made to replace nuclear-armed ICBMs in the hierarchy of global terror. In the end, America and the world would be no more secure than before it squandered its wealth on space-based defense.

Former Secretary of Defense Harold Brown has written, "The prospects for a technical solution to the problem of preserving modern society in the face of an actual thermonuclear war—whether that solution calls for laser antiballistic missile systems in space, elaborate civil defense schemes, or combinations of these with counterforce capability (that is, ways of destroying enemy weapons before they are launched)— seem to me very poor. The effort to attain such technical solutions can itself be quite dangerous if it creates an illusion that a solution has been achieved or is likely to be." [15]

Given all the uncertainties haunting the proposals for space ABMs, the magnitude of the projected costs, and the compelling arguments raised against them, it is difficult to understand just why these proposals have not only been taken seriously, but have been given presidential endorsement and billions of dollars in initial research money. Clearly, something other than rational military or technical thinking is involved, something either sinister or befuddled.

One possibility is that the leading proponents of space ABMs understand their scheme lacks substance. They merely find the language of defense effective rhetoric for mobilizing popular support behind their real aim—initiating an *offensive* arms race in space. Already in the early stages of its work, the Defense Technologies Study Organization, which grew out of Reagan's endorsement of space-based defense, has suggested developing an antisatellite weapon for geostationary orbit as a way to test in the short term the technology required by future ABMs. The rhetoric of defense has much greater appeal than offense. President Reagan, in the speech in which he unveiled his support for missile defense, [16] manipulated the nuclear dread that lies just beneath the surface of his audience's everyday awareness. He asserted that one day technology would remove what technology had wrought, that missile defense would come to replace the balance of terror implicit in the current status quo, mutually assured destruction. By holding out the promise of an end to the nuclear stalemate, and with it its accompanying widespread and chronic low-grade terror, Reagan hoped to win support for his program accelerating the militarization of space. In addition, he may have hoped to coopt the growing antinuclear weapons movement by presenting an acceptable, high-tech military expression of antinuclear feelings. The Reagan administration, enamored with the possibilities of offensive beam weapons in space, may have chosen the smokescreen of missile defense behind which to proceed in developing laser ASATs and space-based laser antiaircraft weapons.

Although it is true that space has been a military zone since the opening of the Space Age, the orbiting of actual satellite weapons would mark a quantum leap from militarization to an actual arms race. Each new offensive weapon developed for space will call forth its defensive countermeasure. That in turn will necessitate improvements in offense. The more military strategists attempt to control the high ground in space, the more control will slip away. Perhaps the point will be reached when neither America nor Russia can afford the arms race any longer, or when the earth's environment can no longer stand the assault of thousands of rockets passing through the fragile upper atmosphere to deploy, maintain, and improve military satellites, or when a mass planetwide peace movement succeeds in stopping it, or when war or social collapse brings about an end to the arms race along with the economies and societies that supported it.

Recognizing its emotional and political appeal, space warriors have adopted antinuclear rhetoric. The same fear and loathing of nuclear weapons that motivates peace activism has been mustered to support and justify the new arms race. The sides have thus been cast for one of the most important political struggles of the future: disarmament versus a new arms race; international cooperation in space or space wars.

The new arms race in space is but another example—perhaps the last one—of leaders refusing to accept the limits of military power, of trying therefore to bring military solutions to bear on what are global political and social crises. The only real hope for national security in the Space Age lies in international security. Global social and political solutions must be sought for the global social and political problems that lead to war.

17

Two Activists for Peace

The men at the Global Technology 2000 Conference in Baltimore in the summer of 1980 calmly listened as experts on one panel discussion after the other predicted the future.[1] No one seemed to doubt the inevitability or desirability of solar powered satellites transmitting energy to earth via concentrated beams of microwaves; of mining operations on the moon and asteroids; of large antennae in stationary orbit making global communications possible via wrist radios; of habitats, factories, and colonies in space. Yet absent from all the projections from current trends was any acknowledgment of two of the most compelling trends of our times: the accelerating arms race between the world's military superpowers and the further consolidation by military establishments of their hold over the allocation of the world's resources. No one seemed to notice that the much-praised vantage point high above the earth not only facilitated global technology development, but also meant that military and police forces could be globally coordinated and centrally commanded and controlled. This vantage point, if exploited, could make possible the dream of every conqueror from Alexander to Hitler— global conquest. Even short of such megalomania, the development of grandiose, expensive space systems in the name of any particular national or commercial interest would invariably lead to the military arguing that such valuable assets need protection from piracy and sabotage. It should have been obvious that, unless trends change, the world of Global Technology 2000 will be a world encircled by arms and anxiety.

Carol Rosin was in attendance at the Baltimore conference. A former corporate vice-president at Fairchild Industries, a leading aerospace corporation, and one of the first women in an executive position in one of the most exclusively male industries in America, she had been a personal assistant to Wernher von Braun until his death in 1975. She had come to the conference to see whether the engineers and scientists there would address the issue of the arms race in space, about which she

172

had grown increasingly concerned. She listened to many panels, particularly those concerning space technology. She was amazed that not one speaker even mentioned the possibility of arms in space. Given an opportunity to question the speakers, Carol rose and challenged them: "Each of you are here representing the industry and the military. Mightn't any one of you address himself to the issue of weapons in space?" Her question was met with the jittery silence of confusion and discomfort.

In spite of the potentially earth-shaking work that they do, speakers at technology conferences are ill-prepared to handle conflict and confrontation. This particular confrontation was even more disconcerting because it involved a woman, an angry and frightened woman who had intruded her emotions into this high-tech sanctuary of masculine propriety. No, no one wanted to address the issue of weapons in space, and certainly no one wanted to get into an argument with her. No one even mustered up a speech about the Soviet threat and the need for a strong national defense in space. The chairman of the panel suggested they move on to another question.

Doctor Robert Bowman was chairman of a session at the conference entitled "Orbital Systems 2000." Bob had been director of Advance Space Programs Development for the Air Force's Space and Missile Systems Organization, where, among other projects, he oversaw the laser weapons program. He went on to become the manager of General Dynamics Corporation's Advanced Space Programs Division. He had twenty years in the field and had acquired technical know-how, respect from his colleagues, awards, honors, and power. He was brilliant, youthful, almost stereotypically calm and self-assured, and gifted with physical attributes that, even without his skill and energy, would have given him access to an elite whose hidden ideologies of power continue to idealize the Nordic-Aryan male—tall, fair, and strong. But Bob suffered from a tragic flaw. He concerned himself with the ends to which his work would be put. When he heard Carol Rosin challenging the panelists, he found himself agreeing with her—not publicly yet, but agreeing nonetheless.

Bob Bowman was particularly concerned about the U.S. antisatellite weaponry. Having been privy to the information on which Air Force planners were basing their estimates of Soviet power, he knew that the United States air-launched ASAT missile was far more capable than the space interceptor the Soviets had deployed. Because the American ASAT would give no warning and need not be predeployed in space, tests of the F-15–launched missiles, which Bowman knew to be near at hand, would immediately raise tensions in space. Once the U.S. ASAT had been tested, the next time a Soviet satellite was accidentally struck by an orbiting piece of the ever more widespread space trash or a meteor—even if it just suffered a breakdown—the Soviets might think their satellite had been attacked. If the destroyed satellite was for early warning, the Soviets might mistake its destruction as a sign of impending attack. Uncertainty is always a factor in space. ASAT weapons would surely aggravate the uncertainty.

In an age of microsecond responses, with military computers evaluating situations as they occur, the inability to distinguish between accidents and attacks would greatly increase the risk of accidental nuclear war on earth and make the outbreak of war in space a constant threat. Even short of actual combat, the tensions aroused by daily uncertainties would negate any hope for international cooperation in space. With heightened dangers and uncertainties in space, it would be all the more difficult to attract investment capital to the commercial and industrial ventures in space that the men at the conference were describing. And they would be unlikely to receive government funds already committed to costly space warfare systems. The construction, testing, and deploying of ASAT weapons and other weapons in space could very well cancel the ambitious plans of the space enthusiasts at the conference. Like children building castles at the ocean's edge at low tide, the dreamers at the Global Technology 2000 Conference were constructing elaborate visions of the future happily ignorant of the threat of destruction near at hand.

With little of his usual self-confidence, Bob Bowman sought out the woman who had raised the question of weapons. He found her in the hallway of the conference center and introduced himself as a military man by profession and temperament. His specialty was designing large space platforms for stationary orbit, and he had some ideas about how space systems could be used to promote peace and global development. He hated to see his ideas negated by a new arms race in space. He told her he'd like to discuss the issues further with her. He was honest right away about being afraid of the implications of his own thinking. He and his wife had seven children, and in his career he had earned respectability, a respectability he could quickly lose by agreeing with her. But he did agree that a way had to be found to stop the weapons race in space. He asked her if there were more people like herself from the industry who felt the same way. He was already sensing that he might be very much alone.

Carol was pleased and more than a little surprised by Bowman. For years she had felt alone among aerospace industry people, ever since she'd angrily resigned from Fairchild. Over coffee in the snack bar, Bob told her about his years in the Air Force, told her how he felt secure at General Dynamics; he had brought the company a lot of new business, particularly in the area of satellite communications. The two of them sat in the cafeteria, surrounded by the intrigue of contracts and money and influence. Bob sucked noisily on his ever-present pipe as Carol talked about the training she'd received from Wernher von Braun. She left out the story of her conflicts with Fairchild and her resignation. She could foresee already, from hearing Bowman talk, that sooner or later he too would have his problems with the industry.

Carol had gone from schoolteacher to corporate executive overnight, living out an unlikely feminist version of the American dream. There were times now when she longed to be back in her sixth-grade classroom, where challenges came in sizes small enough to embrace. There, space travel took place mostly in the imaginations of her students, who were eager to go somewhere brand-new where they could live out their most appealing childhood fantasies.

Rosin had been a remarkable teacher. She knew she was good at what she did. She'd asked for and been given classroom challenges others avoided. The class that became her launch pad into the corporate world was in Arlandria, Virginia, in a flood-prone area where only the poor lived. At Cora Kelly Elementary School she had had sixth-graders as old as fifteen or sixteen, just waiting to reach the legal age for dropping out. After attempting a number of teaching approaches, she'd hit upon something that seemed to work. She asked her children if they would like to take a trip to outer space. For the remainder of the year the classroom was gradually transformed into a spaceship. The students eagerly prepared for their imaginary journey. They plotted their route through the solar system and so learned astronomy. They decided what food they would need to take along and even began to grow sprouts in the closet. They learned about the effects of weightlessness and motion on their bodies and so learned human biology. They calculated flight trajectories and learned algebra. They took on jobs, becoming doctors, engineers, artists, and even space lawyers and judges who enforced one of the first rules the students had passed for space life: All guns and knives must be left behind on earth. As the school year drew to a close and the day of lift-off approached, the students brought suitcases from home. Some actually seemed to believe they were leaving.

The following year Carol repeated her space flight curriculum. When desegregation came to Virginia and she and her students were bused out of Cora Kelly to the rich white schools in Alexandria, Carol brought her program with her. Standardized achievement tests showed that Carol's students, despite being among the poorest in the state, consistently scored the highest in her region.

Such success at a time when the media were reporting on the decline of competency in the schools earned Carol national attention. A UPI story about her program caught the eye of a Fairchild executive. Fairchild's corporate headquarters were in Maryland, not far from where Carol taught. It was 1972. The executives at Fairchild were concerned about the decline of public interest in space and about the industry's faltering public image. The drama of the moon landing was over. Doubts were widespread about technology's ability to solve the most difficult and entrenched of the world's problems. Every technological solution seemed to come complete with a whole new set of problems. At Fairchild, the new public distrust of technology was perceived as a potential threat to corporate visions of future growth. The fact that a teacher in Arlandria, Virginia, could motivate her students to learn all sorts of difficult material by offering them a trip on just the kind of space vehicle Fairchild executives liked to think of themselves producing in the future . . . well, it countered the antitechnologists and those who advocated limited growth. Carol Rosin was hired as corporate manager of Community Relations.

At Fairchild she met Wernher von Braun. Throughout the 1950s and 1960s, Von Braun was the most active and most successful promoter of the space program in the United States. His devotion to rocketry and space flight had a religious quality to it. To Von Braun and many of his followers, the heavens were literally technology's heaven. Space was an empty blackboard on which humanity would someday write the tale of its own conscious evolution. That he had worked first for the German and then for the American military was but a matter of convenience and duty to a man whose eyes were fixed on the stars. It was Von Braun's giant Saturn rocket that had taken American astronauts to the moon. And as NASA's chief of advanced planning, it was Von Braun who most convincingly tried to sell Congress and the American people on sponsoring a voyage to Mars, his lifelong quest. But after NASA's planetary travel plans fell through in the post-Apollo malaise, Von Braun, along with a number of the remainder of his V-2 followers, left the space agency and joined industry, spreading out among a number of different corporations in hopes of finding support there.

By the time he met Carol Rosin, Von Braun knew he was dying of cancer. He saw in the young teacher the enthusiasm for space and education for which he himself had once been famous. He looked to her as someone who might present his ideas to the public and carry on his work after he was gone. Von Braun had done more than any person to bring the world into the Space Age. But at the end of his life, he watched the space technology he had helped develop being turned away from the planets and stars to be increasingly exploited for the weapons of war. Already in the mid-1960s he had warned that "space war would be collective suicide, total ruin even for the one who started it." As he faced his cancer and the deeds of his life, understanding that he would not live to see the voyage to Mars he had long dreamed possible, he turned his work toward technologies that might benefit the people of the earth, particularly the poor. His major project at Fairchild was the ATS-6 (Advanced Technology Satellite). He helped make the arrangements between the company and the governments of the United States and India for sponsoring an ATS in stationary orbit above the Indian subcontinent. With American assistance the Indian government used the satellite to begin a program of broadcasts to bring classes on agricultural techniques, hygiene, birth control, and information from the central government into rural Indian villages via small, inexpensive ground receivers. After his frequent visits to India, Von Braun was, as he told Carol, struck by the children and their hunger-filled eyes. His relationship with his own children was bad. By his own admission, he had been a tyrant in his home. With the time he had left, he was dedicating his work to the children of India.

Among her jobs at Fairchild, the one Carol liked the most was explaining and promoting the educational possibilities of the company's ATS satellites. Besides the work in India, experimental programs had

been carried out on two-way communications between doctors in remote areas of Alaska and medical centers in the city, which provided
access to medical information for areas heretofore inaccessible. Students in Maryland and Colorado had communicated with each other in
two-way tele-education projects. Carol was sent out by Von Braun to
speak wherever people would listen to what he believed were the limitless educational and economic benefits of satellite communications. At
first he told her what to say and how to say it. Whenever she spoke
about space and satellites as an international global resource, she took a
further step in believing it strongly herself. Soon she no longer needed
Von Braun's coaching. She was a brilliant educator and, as with Von
Braun, her enthusiasm was contagious.

The problem arose when she not only began believing what she was
being paid to preach, but grew committed to it. She also began to
understand that Fairchild was using her to make the company look good
through its one international and socially beneficial project. The bulk
of Fairchild's attention and contracts actually went toward the production of the tools of war. She looked closely and saw that the other work
Fairchild did was turning her space dreams to nightmares.

Within weeks after Von Braun's death, Fairchild reorganized its
management to give full attention to marketing its advanced A-10
bomber to take advantage of the lucrative market in arms sales to the
Third World. The ATS-6 project was abandoned. And the ATS-7, the
back-up satellite, rather than being placed in orbit, was put in storage.
Carol was told she was being transferred to the sales team for the A-10,
which was then being promoted to the shah of Iran.

She confronted the executives at the meeting where the reorgan-
ization was announced. "Is there no one here who will explain to me
why we are not going to build and promote education and commercial
communications satellites?" When nobody volunteered an explanation,
she proceeded: "Here we all sit in the War Room"—the name by which
Fairchild's managers referred to their conference room—"while this
industry is leading the planet to destruction. It's as simple as that. And
each of you is responsible. You are making decisions to go in a direction
that I simply cannot follow. Please consider this my resignation."

She walked out of Fairchild alone. Although some of her friends in
the company agreed with her privately, no one would support her
publicly. Most of the managers believed she had behaved rather badly,
behaved like a woman in fact, and had presented further proof to them

that a woman's place was not in the emotion-free, ultraconceptual world of high technology. After all, who was she? A grammar school teacher that some well-intentioned executive had brought out of the classroom and into the War Room in an attempt to make the company look good in the feminist 1970s.

After leaving Fairchild, Rosin worked free-lance for a number of major aerospace firms. One corporation hired her to do a study detailing the position of every member of Congress on the Clean Water Act. The reason, she discovered, was to identify those members who might oppose new missile construction in the western desert because the construction would deplete an already scarce water supply. Finding it almost impossible to get work in the aerospace industry that didn't involve weapons, she soon left her consulting work. Shortly afterward, she attended the Global Technology 2000 Conference, partly in hopes of finding others in the industry—engineers, scientists, managers—who would work with her to help stop what she had come to call the weaponization of space.

For the first few months after Carol Rosin and Bob Bowman met, they spoke to each other frequently, trying to help each other gain an understanding of the dynamics of the arms race. They went over the usual list of causes: American fear of the Soviets, Soviet fear of the Americans, military fantasies of global conquest, greed among the aerospace corporations, the childish fascination with war toys, and just plain ignorance. Bob suggested that the two of them try to come up with an alternative to the arms race, some form of international security system that would utilize the skills and expertise of aerospace engineers and space scientists and embrace the technology for the purposes of peace. Bob had already been planning to attend the thirty-second meeting of the International Astronautical Association, to be held in Rome in September 1981. Perhaps, he suggested, he and Carol could come up with a plan that they could present as a paper at the international meeting.

The task they set for themselves was ambitious. First, they would point to the kinds of functions space systems might be asked to perform in an international peace-monitoring system as an alternative to the arms race. Second, they would propose initial steps toward international cooperation in space that might lead to peace monitoring. Third, they would demonstrate how the aerospace industry would remain vital and healthy through a conversion program that would shift the industry from producing weapons to producing scientific spacecraft and large space platforms for peaceful purposes. They worked on the paper for six months, occasionally disagreeing over the wording, challenging each other to develop a particular idea further. Bob's major interests were in large stationary space platforms, Carol's in the potential of space flight to expand the human imagination. Together they worked out a model proposal that included the use of international reconnaissance radar and photography to provide information to all participating nations, thus giving experience in international cooperation and providing tension-reducing knowledge about international military activities.

Under the unassuming title "The Socioeconomic Benefits of a Global Space Applications Program,"[2] they prepared their paper. When it was completed, Bob fulfilled his obligation to the management and public relations people at General Dynamics and gave them a copy, as was required of an employee who planned to address a public forum. He was prepared for a fight with them, but to his surprise the paper came back, approved without comment. (He would later discover that no one had actually read it.)

The International Astronautical Association meetings are among the few occasions when aerospace engineers, scientists, and government and business people from around the world, East and West, meet to share ideas. It is a time for renewing friendships, making contacts and contracts, and playing the espionage game. At the September 1981 meeting held in Rome the hotels were alive with tourists and with engineers and scientists who had dedicated their lives to things un-earthly. The skies were so blue they could almost see hints of dark purple out at the edges of the atmosphere. The streets were bustling and fragrant with bread and dust, café espresso, and Fiat exhaust. The delegates clustered in small groups, first with their own countrymen, then with international allies, and then with people pursuing the same interests: rockets, vehicles, computers, power systems. The camaraderie at such gatherings belies the fact that most of the participants spend the bulk of each working day preparing and organizing the means of each other's destruction. No doubt they supposed that if war came, it would end, and that in another year they would all meet again, sadder for the losses, regretful for having done nothing to avoid them, disillusioned with the purposes to which their talents had been put, but still witty and charming and brilliant—the same men, now perhaps working for different governments, placing their work at the service of new allegiances.

Whatever happened, the endlessly fascinating problems of guidance, control, power, telemetry, navigation, and information would still be the same. They had to believe that, come a war, they would survive to meet again, minds happily engaged in emotionally neutral tasks. In truth, they were doing little to avoid a war that might leave the earth someday as barren as the moon.

There were a great many speeches scheduled at the conference, and Bob and Carol wanted theirs to stand out in the crowd. Since Bob was an amateur actor in community theater and had a feel for drama, he decided to deliver the address almost as a theatrical presentation. He worked over the paper, turning it into a script. They would deliver it as a team, this passage for Carol, the next for Bob, and the most important points they would make together. He hoped that this departure from normal oratory would force people to take notice.

The night before the speech was to be given, they practiced their assigned lines. On the blank wall of the room in front of them, they placed name tags representing the individuals they most wanted to address in the hall: the heads of the Soviet and American delegations, Bob's boss at General Dynamics, and writer Bob Salkeld, a vigorous supporter of space war. They marked their papers with cues to remind them at which points they would look directly at Salkeld, the Soviets, or the Americans.

The next day Bowman was more nervous than he ever remembered being. Carol was less so. She had little to lose. She knew she would probably never work in the industry again. But this was Bob's coming out as a spokesman for peace, and he knew that his relationship to the industry would never be the same again. Carol offered to give the speech alone, but Bowman dismissed the idea. When the time came for them to ascend the stage, they took deep breaths, went to the podium together, and began, Bob speaking first. "Space's most bountiful product has been information about the earth and its ecosphere. Land surveillance systems make it possible to detect forest fires, crop infestations, blights, droughts, oil slicks, and other dangers. Land surveillance can help planners increase the world's food supply and find new mineral resources on both land and sea."

There was nothing new or controversial here. By and large the emphasis in space had shifted from the stars and planets to looking back down on earth. But just as earth concerns dominated space programs, earth conflicts threatened to become space conflicts. They continued:

Growing antisatellite threats will inevitably lead to defensive and counteroffensive measures. Space-to-space weapons will inexorably lead to weapons directed back at earth. Man's new frontier will then become the lemmings' cliff over which he plunges to his destruction. This must not be allowed.

Fortunately, there are ways that such an eventuality can be avoided. First, and of utmost importance, an expanded agreement on the peaceful uses of outer space must be negotiated and implemented. It must contain an effective ban on antisatellite weapons, either earth-based or space-based, and on spaceborne weapons of all kinds.

They suggested an alternative, a global space applications program based on the model of the International Satellite Communications Corporation (INTELSAT). INTELSAT is owned jointly by 106 countries and provides services to 135. Rosin and Bowman suggested a global satellite system of observation platforms in space to provide information on world food supply and environmental conditions in particular in the oceans and the atmosphere.

One common objection to such a system is that it could too easily produce information of military intelligence value. What is required is that military security be recognized as yet another global problem seeking a global solution. Why, then, shouldn't a global system provide military intelligence about all nations to all nations? This is perhaps the major element in an international peacekeeping system, perhaps the ultimate socioeconomic benefit of space.

With one voice, the two speakers told their audience, "We must see that this last frontier of space does not become a final battleground." They were sure now that they had the complete attention of everyone in the hall. Their early jitters were long gone. They stood and spoke with self-confidence as they encouraged their colleagues not to "underestimate your power to influence the course of events. Raise your voice among your colleagues in favor of programs which would benefit our world, and against those that would imperil it." Finally, as though predicting the censorship he would later receive, Bowman told them, "We must support each other in this endeavor. We must not tolerate even rare abuses of human rights which attempt to silence those who speak out in behalf of all of us. We are a universal family of scientists, engineers, and visionaries—sisters and brothers all—who dare to look to the stars and dream of humanity's venture into space, a peaceful venture for the benefit of this tiny blue island planet and for all of us who call it home."

At first, the crowd responded with a thoughtful silence. Then there was a weak tentative applause, and then a thunderous ovation. The speakers had touched a place in these colleagues that was not yet hardened by power and cynicism. They wanted to believe that their work could truly be a benefit to the world. Perhaps this issue, the grotesqueness of filling the heavens with permanently orbiting weapons of war, weapons outside the control of human hands, would finally transform their work toward peace.

Many of the delegates were amazed that Bowman, representing the General Dynamics Corporation, was free to speak out against space weapons. Most people knew that Bowman's company earned two-thirds of its income from the Pentagon through such diverse projects as the Trident submarines built by their Electric Boat Division, military communications satellites built by the Convair Division, where Bob Bowman was manager, and even the F-15s, which would launch the United States' antisatellite missiles. General Dynamics' top space administrator, James Beggs, had recently been named by Ronald Reagan to head NASA. Yet in the afterglow of enthusiasm evoked by the speech it was possible to imagine that peace and cooperation might become a major corporate goal even of General Dynamics. Bowman told the skeptics that his boss was in the audience and that everything Bowman had said was approved in advance.

Many people came up to the speakers after it was over. Some asked for copies of the speech; others urged them to attend the United Nations Conference on the Exploration and Peaceful Uses of Outer Space (UNISPACE 82) scheduled to take place in Vienna the following summer. On the way back to their hotels, they rode with the delegation from General Dynamics. No one in the car talked about the speech or its reception, but the tension made it obvious that Bob's bosses were displeased.

Within two months after the IAA conference Bowman discovered that his job description at General Dynamics was changing. And he was no longer going to have General Dynamics' permission to speak in public. Three months after he and Carol spoke in Rome, Bob Bowman resigned from General Dynamics to take a job as vice-president of the Space Communications Company. SPACECOM owns and operates NASA's Tracking and Data Relay Satellite System (TDRSS). Although the military plans to make use of the system, SPACECOM had no direct contractual arrangements with the Pentagon, and Bowman believed that his new company would allow him to continue his activities in support of international cooperation in space. Furthermore, he had some ideas he thought would bring SPACECOM business and get the company involved in cooperative international efforts.

But shortly after he joined the company, Bowman was told to forget about joint endeavors between SPACECOM and representatives from other nations. Bowman's subsequent decision to leave was accelerated when he learned that the company was preparing to make a move into the contract competition for laser weapons systems and that they had hired him because of his Air Force connections with the laser program. When he was instructed to hire a certain individual because of his expertise in laser weapons research, Bowman balked. When SPACE-COM executives refused to grant him leave to attend UNISPACE 82, leave that would have been routinely granted for any other kind of conference, it became clear that there might not be anywhere for him in the industry. His stay at Space Communications lasted six months. When he went to UNISPACE in Vienna, he was representing the Friends World Committee for Consultations, an international service organization of the Quakers and one of the nongovernmental organizations recognized by the United Nations for UNISPACE.

UNISPACE 82 was the first special conference on the exploration and peaceful uses of outer space held in over a decade. It was an attempt to reach an international consensus on ways that space technology could best serve the needs of development in the Third World. The major issues to be addressed had been under discussion at the United Nations and in other international forums for years. They included the use and future availability of satellite slots in geostationary orbit. (The unique and valuable fixed-satellite orbit over the equator was already becoming crowded, largely with military communications satellites, and could easily be filled if plans proceeded for large radar platforms and geostationary battle stations.) The use and distribution of information from civilian reconnaissance satellites was also scheduled for discussion, as well as control over the content and use of television signals from direct broadcast satellites that crossed over national boundaries. Another major issue to be dealt with at UNISPACE was the transfer of technology from the few space-faring nations to the earthbound many. But even if agreement could be reached on the many controversial political and economic issues involved, any hope that existed for using space technology for scientific research and peaceful development would be eliminated by an arms race in space between the superpowers. So despite U.S. and Soviet efforts to keep militarization off the UNI-SPACE agenda, it was clear militarization was a, if not the, major concern of the delegates scheduled to meet in Vienna in August.

It had been assumed that the United States would play a major role in the conference. However, the Reagan administration adopted a policy of obstruction. At first, the United States announced that it would boycott UNISPACE over a squabble about staffing at the U.N. Committee for the Peaceful Uses of Outer Space. Early in 1982 the administration dropped its boycott threat and announced it would participate. Bob Bowman spoke to the American delegates prior to UNISPACE and warned them that what he had learned suggested that space militarization would be a major topic, so the United States ought to be prepared with a position and a draft proposal to offer. But the only instructions on the issue the delegates received from the Reagan administration was to refuse to discuss it—space weaponry was properly the province of the U.N. Committee on Disarmament. Although technically correct, the U.S. position ignored the mood of the vast majority of delegations and was also transparently hypocritical, since the United States had been steadfast in its opposition to the creation of a working group in the U.N. Committee on Disarmament to discuss disarmament in space. The United States had insisted all along that such a working group would be premature.

The Soviet Union had originally joined the United States in opposition to discussing militarization at UNISPACE. But by the time the conference convened, the Soviets had joined the majority of delegates in calling for negotiations for an early agreement to prevent an arms race in outer space. The Soviets were able to stand on their record of proposing a draft U.N. treaty banning all weapons in space and on their call to reopen ASAT limitation talks. This isolated the United States, the only power blocking progress in this area.

Bob Bowman, representing the Friends World Committee for Consultations, and Carol Rosin, representing the International Association of Educators for World Peace, went to UNISPACE with specific goals in mind: first, to join with other nongovernment-organization representatives to assure that the issue of weapons in space was not ignored; second, to see that the Soviets and Americans understood the depth of world concerns on this issue; and third, to get a statement out of the conference that the two space superpowers recognized their responsibility to assure peace in space.

At the opening sessions of UNISPACE the first three speakers made the military use of space their main point. Almost every delegate identified it as a major issue in his or her opening statements. The tone of the conference was set early. But despite the mood of the conference delegates, the United States continued to refuse to discuss the issue. Debate over whether or not to talk about weapons in space put the conference way behind schedule. The U.S. delegates, however, received no further instructions from Washington other than to forestall any conference statement mentioning the militarization of space. Even efforts to include such noncommittal language as would be contained in a statement of concern over arms in space were blocked by the American delegation. Only toward the end of the two-week gathering did the United States agree to a compromise wording that stated, "The extension of an arms race into outer space is a matter of grave concern to the international community." But there was no evidence that the government in Washington was about to behave as if it really was concerned about the space arms race. There was no indication that it would, as its delegation had finally agreed, "contribute actively to the goal of preventing an arms race in outer space and to refrain from any action contrary to that aim." [3]

After UNISPACE both Bob Bowman and Carol Rosin returned to Washington, where they went to work trying to convince their former colleagues and their government of the dangers of weapons in space. Bowman set up the Institute for Space and Security Studies as a research and resource organization to provide information on space militarization. Carol Rosin, along with Worldwatch Institute senior researcher Daniel Deudney, formed the Institute for Security in Cooperation in Space (ISCOS) as a public interest research organization devoted to exploring international peace-monitoring satellite systems as an alternative to the arms race in space. (See Appendix 2.)

18

Disarming the Heavens

Despite the trend toward increased militarization, it is not too late to stop the arms race in space. The years 1984 to 1988 will be crucial. During these years, major decisions about America's future course in space will be made. The Pentagon will crystallize its space warfare doctrine. Space weapons will be tested. Vested interests will acquire still more interest. The Air Force will complete construction of its shuttle launch facilities at Vandenburg Air Force Base. The Consolidated Space Operations Center at the Aerospace Defense Command Headquarters in Colorado Springs will become operational. Space shuttle flights may well be routinized, occurring as frequently as monthly or more. The United States' air-launched antisatellite system will be tested and may be deployed. And throughout these years worldwide public awareness of military activities in space will grow.

Billions will have been spent building the military space hardware and designing the systems *before* any public debate takes place. By the time the American people become aware of what the Pentagon has planned, the momentum of the space arms race may have already become unstoppable. But space systems involve lead times and expenses far beyond what the military normally faces. And even though the trends of the late 1970s and early 1980s seem to assure that the heavens will be bristling with arms in the 1990s, these trends are not irreversible. A host of political, fiscal, environmental, technological, and perhaps even moral obstacles stand between military futurism and actual military operations. Concerned people, by organizing an opposition to the militarization of space that highlights and encourages these obstacles, could delay and even halt the trend toward arming the heavens.

The current round of space militarization is, in many important respects, a direct result of the counterforce capabilities of the MX and Trident II long-range ballistic missiles. Silo-busting missiles are worthless against empty silos. The pinpoint accuracy of MX and Trident II are valuable only in a first-strike attack or as part of a protracted nuclear

187

war scenario in which the Soviets are holding back missiles for subsequent attacks. Some military critics have suggested that protracted nuclear war scenarios were invented precisely in order to justify the development of new strategic missiles. Once the missiles were under development, military doctrine evolved to prepare for their use in protracted war. But as Bob Bowman, former director of what is now the Air Force Space Division, wrote, "Once policy and strategy had been changed to accommodate the MX and a protracted, limited nuclear exchange scenario adopted, military strategists realized to their horror that the space systems upon which their 'war-fighting' capability depended were not survivable in a conflict situation."[1]

Without question, the upgrading of America's satellite systems to qualify them for participation in protracted limited nuclear war is the largest single element in America's military space program for the 1980s. Opposition to the arms race in space cannot be separated from opposition to the deployment of the MX and Trident II. If political resistance to the new generation of strategic weapons were to succeed, military strategists would be forced to back away from nuclear war–fighting doctrines and perhaps be forced to turn to nuclear war prevention instead. Without the nuclear first-strike scenario that includes the destruction of Soviet warning satellites, perhaps ASAT weapons could be shelved and a treaty banning all weapons in space could be signed.

A mutual and verifiable Soviet-American freeze on the production and deployment of new strategic nuclear weapons would accomplish more than anything else toward preventing a space arms race. People concerned about the future peaceful use of space and space exploration should work closely with the national freeze campaign or other antinuclear weapons political movements. However, it may be that entrenched political and economic interests with powerful Washington allies have too much at stake in accelerating the arms race to expect much change to be initiated *at the top* of the political structure. But widespread, courageous antinuclear activism—from petitioning to civil disobedience—might be effective in turning nuclear policy away from war-fighting preparations.

The more grandiose space weapons proposals have the least amount of solid political support. Doubts about their practicality persist. In the case of space ABMs in particular, many legislators express concern over potential violations of treaties America has signed. A fiscally conscious Congress may be reluctant to commit grand sums of futuristic technology development in times of tight money. Therefore, support for large-scale space weaponry could dissolve in the face of public opposition. However, at this writing, most members of Congress seem to believe that space issues are exotic policy matters best left to NASA and the Pentagon. By far, most of the active lobbying concerning space issues has come from supporters of space arms: aerospace-industry lobbyists, representatives of right-wing think tanks, Air Force public affairs spokespeople, and various marginal fanatics (one such group is comprised of the followers of Lyndon La Rouche, former head of the U.S. Caucus of Labor Committees, a shadowy political cult once organized around hatred of the Rockefellers. La Rouche and his followers became nominal Democrats with dreams of one day taking over the party. The issue they've adopted for the eighties is support of space weapons and other large-scale space programs. The source of their organization's significant funds is a mystery.) But despite the lack of a true popular base of support in Congress, spacewar proponents have prevailed due largely to the lack of organized opposition. Without the money available to the industry and Air Force lobbyists, opponents of space weapons need to link their opposition with a vocal and sustained grass-roots peace activism to force Congress to rethink its multibillion-dollar commitment to space weaponry.

Still, the most ambitious and expensive of the spacewar proposals could be defeated by popular opposition. Space projects tend to depend on each other for their justifications. If the most ambitious projects, such as space laser weapons, were stopped or limited to research only, the momentum of the space arms race would be reversed. This is due in part to Schriever's "dilemma," which continues to haunt military space planning. Space operations will remain extremely expensive for the foreseeable future. Operational costs will be reduced when, and only if, space operations become routinized by a reusable transportation infrastructure. But the price of creating and maintaining all the necessary parts of a space infrastructure would be astounding—at least $50 to $100 billion dollars might need to be spent between 1985 and 1995. An operational space infrastructure would consist of: a space station in low-earth "parking" orbit; in-space construction capabilities; an orbit-to-orbit shuttle, a space "tug"; a reliable means to carry large structures to geostationary orbit; and a source of in-space power.

The space shuttle was originally conceived of as but one segment in a space transportation system (STS) to open space to routine use. But cost overruns and technical problems resulted in the shuttle segment exhausting the funds meant to finance the entire system. At present the STS is a fragment of a system. Schriever's dilemma remains valid. The military can't justify the expense of building the rest of the space infrastructure unless it has a clear mission in space that requires it. Yet they can't commit themselves to developing the weapons systems for space missions without cost-effective transportation. Futuristic space weapons such as laser battle stations, space ABMs, and Schriever's space-based radar system serve the same purpose, defining future missions in space. These missions then in turn justify developing the infrastructure. If political opposition was to interject itself into this neat arrangement of interdependencies, the entire structure of military space planning might begin to unravel. Without the spacewar schemes, justification for the complex space infrastructure would be weakened. The converse is equally true. If political opposition were mobilized against vast expenditures in space for space stations, space tugs, and future manned transporters, then the Air Force's future mission in space would have to be radically simplified.

Given Schriever's dilemma, organized and creative opposition to the arms race in space has a good chance of succeeding. The defeat of proposals for large-scale space weapons could undermine rationales behind the military's involvement in building a space transportation infrastructure. NASA, after reestablishing its independence as a civilian agency, would then be required to sell its programs to the American people on their merits. A public debate on the future course of the U.S. space program could then be held independent of hidden military agendas.

If military space activity can be stopped, delayed, or disrupted, it will become more difficult for strategists to plan for survivable nuclear war. The belief that such a war can be limited and controlled will be undercut if military space activity can be limited to attack warning and treaty verification. In addition, a slowdown in the military space race might raise again the possibility of international cooperation in the exploration of outer space and restimulate what could be a great human adventure if carried out by people representing the planet rather than parochial national interests. Further international cooperation could lead to the establishment of an international surveillance satellite system to monitor crises situations and to provide independent information about global military activities of all nations to all nations.

The first step in disarming the heavens would be to begin negotiations toward an international treaty banning weapons in space. Representative Joe Moakley (a Democrat from Massachusetts) has twice introduced legislation "calling for the president to immediately engage in negotiations with the Soviet Union toward a complete and verifiable ban of weapons of any kind in space or based elsewhere for use against space targets." The resolution also calls on the president to "vigorously pursue multilateral talks aimed at banning all weapons from space (launched by any nation) through the appropriate organs of the United Nations, including, but not limited to, establishment of a working group within the UN Committee on Disarmament to provide a forum for discussion of this topic leading to a verifiable treaty." By mid-1983 Congressman Moakley had succeeded in adding seventy co-sponsors to the legislation.

The Institute for Security in Cooperation in Outer Space (ISCOS) has begun formulating a space arms control agenda and a new space security agenda. Daniel Deudney, one of the founders of ISCOS, and a senior researcher at the Worldwatch Institute, delivered the following statement on U.S. military space policy to the Senate Foreign Relations Committee.

The present arms control regime for space weapons—the *Limited Test Ban Treaty*, the *ABM Treaty* and the *Outer Space Treaty* has worked remarkably well, but contains important loopholes through which space weapons can pass. To abandon these treaties because of their loopholes would be like dynamiting a leaky dike at high flood rather than plugging the leaks.

Fortunately, we are at a stage where weapons in space can be stopped before they are ever extensively tested and deployed. Space weapon development is no further along than air war was when World War I biplane reconnaissance pilots carried hand guns. Most importantly, because so little has been tested, truly comprehensive controls are relatively easy to construct and verify.

What would a verifiable treaty banning weapons in space look like? First, a treaty banning just anti-satellite weapons and not space weapons generally is not feasible. Trying to ban ASAT's but not more ambitious anti-ballistic missile systems would be like outlawing hand guns while permitting bazookas and machine guns. Second, a treaty should contain both broad prohibitions and careful functional prohibitions. For broad language I would suggest prohibiting:

- the testing, production, deployment, or use of any space-based, air-based, or ground-based weapons system that is designed to damage, destroy, or interfere with the functioning of any spacecraft of any nation; and
- the stationing in orbit around the Earth, on any celestial body, or at any other location in outer space of any weapon that has been designed to inflict injury or cause any other form of damage on the Earth, in the atmosphere, or on objects placed in space.

To effectively outlaw weapons, a treaty should outlaw the following observable activities and capabilities (or Functionally Related Observable Differences "FRODs" in the language of SALT):

- *forbid explosions and unmanned orbital rendezvous* by two satellites of the same country. (This would ban the USSR's orbital rendezvous ASAT.)

- *forbid collisions or close high speed passes.* (This would ban U.S. direct ascent.)

- *forbid close approaches* in geosynchronous orbit. (This would ban space mines.)

- *limit the size of laser mirrors* and the number of maximum-size laser mirrors bundled together. (This would allow laser communications but forbid lasers capable of destroying satellites or missiles.)

- *limit the size of atomic power sources.* (This would effectively foreclose scale-up of directed energy weapons, slow the development of active radar targeting satellites, such as Cosmos 942 and 1307, and protect human health from fallout.)

- *limit electro-magnetic interference.* Present restrictions by the International Telecommunications Union (ITU) should be strengthened and included in an arms control agreement.

The control of weapons in space simply clears the stage for the use of space technology to improve both arms control verification, and our relations with the Soviets. This positive space security agenda emphasizes the unique role of space technology in providing *mutual assured security* and mutual benefits.

First, *expand the use of space for crisis monitoring.* The recently proposed establishment of an orbital joint U.S.-Soviet command center should be a priority. When there are tens of thousands of nuclear weapons, many within minutes of their targets, on perpetual alert status and checked only by unmanned warning satellites and the hotline, it makes eminent sense to exploit "the high frontier" to keep a tighter lid on accident, miscalculation and false alarm.

Second, *establish an International Satellite Monitoring Agency (ISMA).* This idea, proposed by Giscard d'Estaing before the General Assembly in 1978, has been vetoed by U.S. and Soviet opposition. An ISMA would permit the Security Council to monitor crises and border disputes and would lay the groundwork for monitoring compliance with the treaties banning chemical and biological warfare and environmental modification. Depending on whether ISMA obtained technology from the superpowers, a basic monitoring system would cost between $1 billion and $2 billion a year—about the cost of one B-1 bomber. Such an international system would supplement, not substitute for, the national monitoring systems. It is particularly ironic that the United States with its great concern about verification of arms control treaties, has so vigorously opposed expanding access, and gaining international legitimacy for this critical peacekeeping technology.

Third, *conduct joint missions with the Soviets.* Writing in 1976, Bruce Murray, former head of the Jet Propulsion Laboratory and President of the Planetary Society, observed, "The rate of progress in space science may well be dependent on the political fortunes of detente on earth." This greatest adventure of our time—the peaceful exploration of the cosmos—faces a bleak future, declining budgets and preemption of technology by the military both here and in the Soviet Union. Having two separate space programs doing much the same things makes less and less sense. And as costs of missions rise, the need for cooperation grows still further. A series of joint planetary and scientific probes would be a boost both to our sagging programs—and political relations.

Joint manned missions would be even more valuable. A U.S. Administration, looking for a bold, high visibility, quick pay-off way to cut through gathering clouds of suspicion and war, would find a joint U.S.-Soviet manned space mission particularly appealing. Unlike in 1976 when the Apollo-Soyuz rendezvous was a meeting of two parallel systems, the space shuttle and the Salyut stations are perfect complements for each other. What better way to find out what's going on in Soviet space stations or to allay Soviet's suspicions about the shuttle than to take each other for a ride? More routine cooperation in space and the consequent commingling of space scientists would make much harder concealed weapons work.

In conclusion, the world is at a critical juncture. Either we move now to comprehensively ban weapons from space or we will have a major new arms race on our hands. Space technology can be the foundation of an alternative security system—if we ban weapons now.[2]

Despite his cogent arguments, Deudney's recommendations have little near-term chance of being accepted by American policy makers. The Reagan administration's efforts to revive the Cold War have been largely successful. A large segment of the American people can be counted on to support programs in space it perceives as necessary to counter the Soviet threat. As the new Cold War has intensified, the Soviet leadership has reestablished old patterns of fear, distrust, and hostility. Clearly, both sides have good reasons to fear the other. And both sides have internal social and economic problems their leaders wish would go away, but don't. The Cold War makes governing easier by creating enemies everyone can love to hate. Reagan's unprecedented military buildup; his aggressive policies throughout the world; his apparent intention to repudiate the ABM treaty in particular and arms control in general; his encouragement of such space hawks as Edward Teller, Bernard Schriever, and others who believe war with the Soviets is inevitable; and his administration's casual consideration of limited nuclear war scenarios have all combined to provide apparent justification for the Soviets' long-standing fear of the West. The Soviets' police-state mentality, xenophobia, and manic concern with border security have resulted in international tragedies, deceptive rhetoric, and a war in Afghanistan. Both sides' worst fears seem justified. The disintegration of détente has made a reasoned analysis of national security issues almost impossible to achieve. This disintegration must somehow be interrupted. In a world armed for self-destruction, current international tensions are both frightening and self-perpetuating.

Anti-Communist rhetoric and fear mongering will no doubt be used to mobilize support for the military in space. Some of the arguments spacewar proponents use are transparently specious; others are not as obvious. Much is made of a large inequality favoring the Soviets in the number of space launchings. But this statistic merely reflects the fact that the more sophisticated American payloads operate, on the average, twenty times longer while integrated operations mean that fewer American satellites are required for the same number of functions.

Much is also made of the fact that the Soviets have an operational antisatellite weapon, whereas the American ASAT is still under development and may not be deployed before 1987. The Soviet system is a spacecraft that maneuvers close to its target and explodes into a shower of shrapnel. Its target must be in a relatively low-earth orbit—150 to 1400 miles—well below the majority of U.S. military satellites. The United States also had an operational ASAT, with a nuclear warhead. That system was dismantled in 1975 in favor of developing an advanced air-launched system utilizing a two-stage rocket and a miniature guided missile with a conventional warhead launched from beneath an F-15 fighter. The American ASAT is also limited to low altitudes, but more Soviet satellites utilize low orbits than do American.

A number of leaked intelligence reports have claimed that the Soviets are ahead in beam-weapon technology. Since these intelligence leaks are based on restricted information, there is no way to refute or confirm their claims. However, history teaches that it is wise to be skeptical of leaked intelligence reports concerning Soviet military strength. The historical record clearly demonstrates that vested interests frequently manipulate such reports in efforts to tap the federal treasury. When public support was needed to hasten the procurement of the first round of strategic missiles in the 1950s, the "missile gap" was conveniently "discovered" and leaked to the press through erroneous or incomplete intelligence reports. The fabrication of "intelligence" is an art that has been practiced at one time or another by each of the armed service's intelligence divisions. Frequently, such intelligence is used to justify the weapons and strategies favored by a particular service's top command—a simple example of the spies telling the chief the news they think he wants to hear.

The story of the nuclear-powered airplane is a perfect example of this process in action. The airplane was designed with aerodynamically absurd lead shielding between engine and pilot, but with no apparent consideration for what might happen if one day it should crash. In ten years of research and development it soaked up hundreds of millions of dollars before eventually being canceled by Secretary of Defense McNamara in the early sixties. Throughout the years of the nuclear airplane project, spokesmen for the Air Force, the aerospace industry, and the Atomic Energy Commission periodically went to Congress claiming to have evidence that the Soviet Union was leading in the effort to produce nuclear-powered airplanes. As far as anyone knows, no nuclear airplane from East or West ever flew.

The forces pushing the arms race into space are the same forces that were at work in the 1950s: interservice and intercorporate rivalries, military posturing, and simple greed, in addition to genuine concerns for security. These forces make control of the arms race extremely difficult.

But cold wars have thawed in the past. Arms races have slowed. It is possible that concern for peace and planetary survival will prevail over parochial interests.

On July 5, 1969, former President Lyndon Johnson was interviewed by Walter Cronkite. Johnson spoke of how he felt that November evening in 1957 after the Soviets had successfully launched Sputnik I. "That sky that had always been so friendly and had brought us beautiful stars and moonlight and comfort and pleasure all at once seemed to have question marks all over it because of this new development."

The questions raised by the first act of the Space Age are still unanswered. The only certainty is that what we do in space in the next few decisive years of the 1980s will affect generations of life on earth to come.

Appendix 1:

RESOLUTION CALLING FOR IMMEDIATE NEGOTIATIONS FOR A
BAN ON ANY WEAPONS IN SPACE. INTRODUCED IN CONGRESS.

97TH CONGRESS
2D SESSION
H. J. RES. 607

Calling for immediate negotiations for a ban on weapons of any kind in space.

IN THE HOUSE OF REPRESENTATIVES

SEPTEMBER 23, 1982

Mr. MOAKLEY (for himself, Mr. HOLLENBECK, Mr. BROWN of California,
Mr. BEDELL, Mr. FRANK, Mr. MAVROULES, Mr. HORTON, Mr. DOWNEY,
Mrs. SCHROEDER, Mrs. CHISHOLM, Mr. LEACH of Iowa, Mr. LAFALCE, Mr.
WEISS, Mr. SEIBERLING, Mr. FORD of Tennessee, Mr. DENARDIS, Mr.
LOWRY of Washington, Mr. WEAVER, Mr. WOLPE, Mr. DELLUMS, Mrs.
HECKLER, Mr. BRODHEAD, Mr. EDGAR, Mr. LEHMAN, Mr. AUCOIN, Mr.
CROCKETT, Mr. SCHEUER, Ms. MIKULSKI, Mr. FAUNTROY, and Mr.
GREEN) introduced the following joint resolution; which was referred to the
Committee on Foreign Affairs

JOINT RESOLUTION

Calling for immediate negotiations for a ban on weapons of any
kind in space.

Whereas the peaceful exploration of space has greatly benefited
the development of the theoretical and applied sciences and
the continued peaceful exploration of space offers an enormous potential for expanding the limits of our knowledge
and providing additional benefits to the human race;

Whereas mankind's continued preoccupation with developing
weapons of destruction already threatens the quality and existence of life on Earth as we know it;

Whereas the quality and existence of such life will face an even greater threat should the arms race be extended into space; and

Whereas an international agreement to prohibit the introduction of weapons of any kind into space is needed in order to avoid the financial, social, and human costs that could result from such an arms race: Now, therefore, be it

1   *Resolved by the Senate and House of Representatives*
2   *of the United States of America in Congress assembled,*
3   That (a) the President shall resume immediately bilateral
4   talks with the Soviet Union for the purpose of negotiating a
5   comprehensive treaty prohibiting—

6   　　　(1) the testing, deployment, production, or use of
7   　　　any space-based, air-based, or ground-based weapons
8   　　　system which is designed to damage, destroy, or inter-
9   　　　fere with the functioning of any spacecraft of any
10 　　　nation; and

11 　　　(2) the stationing in orbit around the Earth, on
12 　　　any celestial body, or at any other location in outer
13 　　　space of any weapon which has been designed to inflict
14 　　　injury or cause any other form of damage on the
15 　　　Earth, in the atmosphere, or on objects placed in
16 　　　space.

17 Any such treaty shall establish a procedure for verifying com-
18 pliance with its terms.

19 　　　(b) The President shall seek the establishment of a
20 working group within the United Nations Committee on

1 Disarmament or other United Nations body to provide a
2 forum for discussing the issues and problems, including the
3 problem of verifiability, involved in drafting, negotiating, and
4 enforcing the terms of a multilateral space treaty banning
5 from space all weapons launched by any country.

O

Appendix 2:

The following organizations are primarily interested in space and space technology and have expressed concern about the militarization of space.

Campaign for Space
300 M Street SW, Suite 500
Washington, DC 20024

The Campaign for Space is primarily involved in supporting political candidates for federal office who support the space program. The executive director, David Webb, helped coordinate nongovernmental organization participation in the UNISPACE conference and has expressed serious concern about the arms race in space.

High Technology Professionals for Peace
2161 Massachusetts Avenue
Cambridge, MA 02140

This organization has material available on the uses of high tech in war and peace. It attempts to place conscientious professionals in nonmilitary work, not an easy task in the high tech field.

Institute for Security in Cooperation in Outer Space
% Daniel Deudney
Worldwatch Institute
1776 Massachusetts Avenue NW
Washington, DC 20036

A new public-interest research group devoted to exploring alternative space-based security systems.

Institute for Space and Security Studies
7720 Mary Cassatt Drive
Potomac, MD 20854

This organization was founded by Robert Bowman (see Chapter 17) to provide professional information about the issues of space and national security. It supports and lobbies for a treaty banning all weapons in space.

Peaceful Uses of Outer Space
Room 3361-A, United Nations
New York, NY 10017

This is the public information service of the U.N. Committee on the Exploration and Peaceful Uses of Outer Space. It pursues an interest in using space technology to benefit the developing world and is gravely concerned about space weaponry.

The Planetary Society
1440 New York Drive
Altadena, CA 91001

This popular organization is headed by Carl Sagan (of *Cosmos* fame), and is the largest space interest organization. Sagan himself has publicly spoken out against U.S. nuclear policies and the militarization of space. The Planetary Society protests cutbacks in NASA's planetary sciences programs (directly attributable to increased military activity in space) and promotes public awareness and involvement in planetary exploration and the search for extraterrestrial intelligence.

The Progressive Space Forum
1724 Sacramento Street, Suite 105
San Francisco, CA 94109

A national organization, formerly known as Citizens for Space Demilitarization. It is the most politically active, consistent, and intelligent voice in the "pro-space" movement. Their monthly space news report, "Space for All People," is the most important and valuable single source of current information on the arms race in space. Their slogan, "Caring for the Earth, Reaching for the Stars," sums up both their political worldview and the many interesting intellectual contradictions the organization is still working through.

The following organizations are primarily concerned with peace and social justice issues. Many have not yet begun to organize against the arms race in space, though their political and moral foundations will most likely mean they will become involved in the space issue in the mid-1980s.

American Friends Service Committee (AFSC)
National Headquarters
1501 Cherry Street
Philadelphia, PA 19102

AFSC is a Quaker service and educational organization founded in 1917. It received the Nobel Peace Prize in 1947. It has forty regional and area offices throughout the United States. It supports a nuclear freeze and a comprehensive test ban treaty. Its regional office in St. Petersburg, Florida, near the Kennedy Space Center, has been active in educating the public about the issues of weapons in space.

Center for Defense Information
600 Maryland Avenue SW
Washington, DC 20024

This group likes to be known as a supporter of a strong defense. It criticizes anything it believes is excessive in defense. The CDI approaches the issues from a military point of view. In 1980 it published a review of space weapons by Thomas Karras, also author of *The New High Ground: Strategies and Weapons of Space Age War.*

Clergy and Laity Concerned (CALC)
National Headquarters
198 Broadway
New York, NY 10038

A religiously oriented group with forty-nine chapters and action groups working for a just society and a peaceful world. It publishes a newsletter, pamphlets, etc.

Coalition for a New Foreign and Military Policy
120 Maryland Avenue SE
Washington, DC 20002

This group focuses on producing and publishing pamphlets and organizing manuals on disarmament, the military budget, and Latin American issues.

Educators for Social Responsibility
P.O. Box 1041
Brookline Village, MA 02147

A national organization of teachers and other educators focusing on the issues of peace and disarmament.

Fellowship of Reconciliation
P.O. Box 271
Nyack, NY 10960

A religious organization of pacifists. It offers a study guide for churches on disarmament.

Ground Zero
806 15th Street NW, Suite 421
Washington, DC 20005

A national educational and political organization working on disarmament by focusing on the effects of nuclear explosions.

Institute for Defense and Disarmament Studies
251 Harvard Street
Brookline, MA 02140

The institute produces books and publications on disarmament. It is known as the birthplace of the nuclear freeze movement.

Institute for Policy Studies
1901 Q Street NW
Washington, DC 20009

A research and education center. Areas of focus include domestic policy, national security, international economics, and human rights approached from a global perspective.

Institute for World Order
777 United Nations Plaza
New York, NY 10017

This organization produces materials on disarmament and international cooperation.

Jobs With Peace
2490 16th Street
San Francisco, CA 94103

A national organization working to help local and regional groups develop plans for converting military industries to peaceful production.

Lawyers Alliance for Nuclear Arms Control
14 Beacon Street, Suite 719
Boston, MA 02108

The Alliance provides materials to lawyers and their professional organizations on nuclear weapons issues.

Movement for a New Society
4722 Baltimore Avenue
Philadelphia, PA 19143

This group produces excellent material on living daily life in a spirit of non-violent social and political change. It has done much ground-breaking work in creating nonhierarchical organizational structures and devised procedures for holding meetings that replace Roberts' Rules of Order.

Mobilization for Survival
3601 Locust Walk
Philadelphia, PA 19104

An activists' coalition organizing against the next holocaust and for survival. There are local chapters in most major cities.

Nuclear War Education Project
Federation of American Scientists
307 Massachusetts Avenue NE
Washington, DC 20002

This group provides materials by scientists on many aspects of the arms race.

Nuclear Weapons Freeze Campaign Clearinghouse
4144 Lindell Blvd.
St. Louis, MO 63108

The national headquarters for the (nuclear) FREEZE Campaign, the largest single antinuclear weapons campaign in America. The clearinghouse publishes a newsletter and current materials for work on the nuclear freeze.

Physicians for Social Responsibility
National Headquarters
P.O. Box 144
Watertown, MA 02172

A group of doctors organized against what PSR refers to as the final epidemic, nuclear war. Chapters in many cities.

SANE
711 G Street
Washington, DC 20003

SANE publishes a newsletter on peace conversion of the war industry. It works mostly with labor unions.

Science for the People
897 Main Street
Cambridge, MA 02139

This organization publishes an excellent monthly on science and social policy, providing valuable information on the arms race, whether on earth or in space.

Syracuse Cultural Workers Project
P.O. Box 6367
Syracuse, NY 13217

This group produces visual materials—calendars, greeting cards, posters, and slide shows on the themes of disarmament and social changes—and distributes them nationally.

Union of Concerned Scientists
1208 Massachusetts Avenue
Cambridge, MA 02138

A national organization of scientists concerned about social and political issues.

War Resisters League
339 Lafayette Street
New York, NY 10012

A national organization with chapters in many cities. It is one of the oldest, best established radical peace groups, advocating nonviolent direct action to confront the warfare system. The league publishes an organizers' manual and much other material.

Women and Life On Earth
160 Main Street
Northampton, MA 01060

A network of feminist and ecology organizations in the Northeast United States.

Womens' International League for Peace and Freedom
National Headquarters
1213 Race Street
Philadelphia, PA 19107

A well-established peace group. It was very active in the 1950s and 1960s, protesting atmospheric nuclear tests. It remains active, with chapters in most major cities, and publishes a newsletter and provides resources.

The following periodicals provide regular and valuable information on the arms race from a variety of perspectives. Many have begun to give attention to space militarism.

Dollars and Sense
38 Union Square #14
Somerville, MA 02143

Articles frequently look at the issues of disarmament and the arms race in terms of the political economy of militarism.

Guardian
33 West 17th Street
New York, NY 10011

An independent radical newsweekly. Up-to-date information on international affairs and domestic political and social life.

In These Times
1509 North Milwaukee Avenue
Chicago, IL 60622

A weekly newspaper providing its readers with a fresh socialist perspective on the news.

Mother Jones
625 3rd Street
San Francisco, CA 94107

A monthly popular magazine of culture and political insight.

New Age Journal
244 Brighton Avenue
Allston, MA 02134

A monthly magazine that attempts to combine a "new age" spiritual perspective with a radical political critique of American society.

The Nation
72 Fifth Avenue
New York, NY 10011

The oldest and best of the left-wing opinion journals, covering politics, literature, and the arts.

Nuclear Times
298 Fifth Avenue, Room 512
New York, NY 10011

A monthly reporting on the nuclear disarmament movement.

No Nuclear News
Box 149
Somerville, MA 02143

A publication offering reprints on nuclear power, nuclear waste, nuclear weapons, etc. from various periodicals around the country.

The Progressive
409 East Main Street
Madison, WI 53703

An independent voice in the struggle for peace and economic freedom.

Radical America
38 Union Square #14
Somerville, MA 02143

A radical journal of radical law, feminism, labor issues, and international affairs.

Science for the People
897 Main Street
Cambridge, MA 02139

A progressive view of the social and political implications of science and technology.

Space for All People
1724 Sacramento Street, Suite 105
San Francisco, CA 94109

A monthly space-news report from the Progressive Space Forum, extremely valuable for the information it gives on space militarization.

PEACE Newsletter
924 Burnet Avenue
Syracuse, NY 13203

The monthly magazine of the Syracuse Peace Council. It includes articles on national and international issues.

Chapter Notes

INTRODUCTION

1. Lucian of Samosato. "Icaromenypus: An Aerial Expedition." *The Works of Lucian,* Vol. 3 (Oxford, 1905).
2. Author's interview with General Bernard A. Schriever, USAF Retired. Washington, D.C. January 8, 1983.

CHAPTER 1

1. Kurt Debus, chief of V-2 launch operations, later became Chief of Operations for NASA at Cape Canaveral. Krafft Ehricke, consultant to the German A-bomb project and the German rocket team, later became an executive at General Dynamics and annual space lecturer at the Air University Command and Staff School. Walter Scweidetsky, head of the V-2 guidance group, later joined General Dynamics Convair Division, working on ICBM guidance. Hans Maus, a member of the V-2 engineering group, became chief of the executive staff at NASA's Marshall Spaceflight Center. Martin Schilling, chief of the testing lab for the V-2 propulsion division became vice-president for research and development at the Raytheon Corporation. Hans Hosenthein, designer of the V-2's launch and guidance antennae became chief of Flight Dynamics at Marshall Spaceflight Center. Erich Neubert, production manager for V-2 guidance and telemetry labs, later worked for the U.S. Army missile program. Adolph Thiel, V-2 engineer, became vice-president at TRW, Inc. Hubertus Strughold, director of medical research for the Aviation Ministry in Berlin, became chief scientist at the Aerospace Medical Division at Brooks Air Force Base in Texas.
2. Wernher von Braun. "Prelude to Space Travel." in Cornelius Ryan (ed.) *Across the Space Frontier* (New York, 1952), p. 14.
3. "Man Made Moon Is Held Feasible." *New York Times.* 6 December 1952, p. 23.
4. "U.S. Shot at Moon Opposed as Stunt." *New York Times.* 6 June 1958, p. 9.

CHAPTER 2

1. NSC 68. "A Report to the President Pursuant to the President's Directive of January 31, 1950 from the Secretaries of State and Defense." April 7, 1950. TOP SECRET. Declassified February 21, 1975.
2. F. J. Krieger. "Soviet Astronautics." RAND Corporation Paper P-1437, 24 February 1958.
3. Quoted in Walter LaFeber. *America, Russia and the Cold War, 1945-1966* (New York, 1967), p. 178.
4. Quoted in Blanche Wiessen Cook. *The Declassified Eisenhower: A Divided Legacy* (New York, 1981), p. 168.

CHAPTER 3

1. Henry Kissinger's limited-war strategy rested on one of history's more bizarre examples of economic determinism—the soldiers in a capitalist democracy are better able to fight limited nuclear war than their counterparts from Communist dictatorships. "In a limited nuclear war," Kissinger wrote, "dispersal is the key to survival and mobility the prerequisite to success. Everything depends on leadership of high order, personal initiative and mechanical aptitude; qualities more prevalent in our society than in the regimented system of the USSR. To be sure, the Soviet forces can train and equip units for nuclear war. But self-reliance, spontaneity and initiative cannot be acquired by training; they grow naturally out of social institutions or they do not come into being." According to Kissinger, the American free enterprise system with its "superior industrial potential, the broader range of technology and the adaptability of social institutions should give the advantage." For a capitalist nation, "the most productive form of war is to utilize weapons of an intermediary range of destructiveness, sufficiently complex to require a substantial productive effort, sufficiently destructive so that manpower cannot be substituted for technology, yet discriminating enough to permit the establishment of a significant margin of superiority. It would seem that the weapons systems appropriate for limited nuclear war meet these requirements." Henry Kissinger. *Nuclear Weapons and Foreign Policy* (New York, 1957), p. 195.
2. "No Reason to Grow Hysterical. News conference, 10/9/57, Dwight D. Eisenhower." *US News and World Report*, 18 October 1957.
3. Quoted in Richard Hutton. *The Cosmic Chase* (New York, 1981), p. 39.
4. Quoted in Robert Salkeld, *War and Space* (New Jersey, 1970), p. 134.
5. Salkeld. *War and Space*. p. 135.

CHAPTER 4

1. Quoted in Donald Cox and Michael Stoiko. *Spacepower* (Philadelphia, 1958), p. 57.

2. "Military Requirements for Man In Space." President's Science Advisory Committee report. SECRET. Declassified February 11, 1981. Eisenhower Library, White House Office, Office of the Special Assistant for Science and Technology, 1957-61, Box 16, Space Notebook (Piland) 1958-59 (4).

3. Testimony of General Homer Boushey in U.S. Congress. *The Next Ten Years in Space.* Staff Report of the Select Committee in Astronautics and Space Exploration. U.S. House of Representatives. June 1959.

4. Testimony of General Dwight Beach, Director of Guided Missiles and Special Weapons, Office of the Deputy Chief of Staff for Military Operations in U.S. Congress. *Investigation of Government Organization for Space Activities.* Hearings before the Subcommittee on Government Organization for Space Activities of the Committee on Aeronautical and Space Sciences, U.S. Senate, 86th Congress. March–April 1959.

5. U.S. Congress. *Investigation of Government Organization for Space Activities.* p. 135.

CHAPTER 6

1. "U.S. Policy on Outer Space." National Aeronautics and Space Council. Franklyn Phillips, Acting Secretary. Transmittal Note, January 26, 1960. Released September 3, 1981. Eisenhower Library, White House Office, Office of the Special Assistant for National Security Affairs, Records, 1952-66, NSC series, Policy Paper Subseries, Box 25, NSC 581411, Outer Space (1).

2. Quoted in George Robinson. "Space Law, Space War, and Space Exploration." *Journal of Social and Political Studies.* Fall 1980, #3, p. 170.

3. Robinson. *Space Law.* p. 172.

4. John Medaris. *Countdown for Decision* (New York, 1960).

5. U.S. Congress. *Investigation of Government Organization for Space Activities,* p. 333.

6. Ibid., p. 142.

7. Ibid., p. 296.

8. Ibid., p. 400.

9. National Aeronautical and Space Council. "U.S. Policy on Outer Space."

10. Quoted in Lon Schanche. "General of Outer Space." *Saturday Evening Post.* 7 October, 1961, p. 78.

11. U.S. Congress. *Investigation of Government Organization of Space Activities,* p. 403.

12. Quoted in LaFeber. *America, Russia and The Cold War,* p. 219.

CHAPTER 7

1. "More Emphasis on Manned Spacecraft Required." *US News & World Report*, 9 October 1961; "Arms in Space: Something Else to Worry About." *Time*, 9 October 1961; see also Trevor Gardner. "High-Priority Military Space Race Urged." *Aviation Week* 9 October 1961.

2. In 1980 two of the members of this Air Force study committee, Bernard Schriever and Edward Teller, were members of Ronald Reagan's Transition Advisory Team on Science and Technology.

3. U.S. Congress. *Review and Recommendations on the Nation's Space Program*. Committee on Science and Astronautics, U.S. House of Representatives, August 1960.

4. Reported in "Kennedy Group Criticizes Space Effort: Weisner Task Force Report." *Aviation Week*, 23 January 1961.

5. Lyndon Johnson. *The Vantage Point* (New York, 1971).

6. Memorandum, Lyndon B. Johnson, vice-president, to John F. Kennedy, president, May 8, 1961. Enclosed: Recommendations for Our National Space Program. SECRET. Released July 19, 1974. Kennedy Library, POF, Special Correspondence, Lyndon Johnson Folder, Box 30.

7. Quoted in John Logsdon. *The Decision to Go to the Moon: Project Apollo and the National Interest* (Chicago, 1970), p. 5.

CHAPTER 8

1. Quoted in Robert Divine, *Blowing on the Wind: The Nuclear Test Ban Debate 1954–1960* (London, 1978).

2. Memorandum, Neil McElroy, secretary of Defense, to Dwight D. Eisenhower, president, August 5, 1959. SECRET. Declassified February 22, 1979. Eisenhower Library, Papers as President of the United States, 1953–61 (Ann Whitman File), Administration File, Folder: McElroy, Neil H., Secretary of Defense 1959 (2), Box 28.

3. Quoted in Phillip Klass. *Secret Sentries in Space* (New York, 1971).

4. Quoted in "Nuclear Blast Effects Pose New Threat." *Aviation Week*, 19 March 1962.

5. "Scientist in Britain Fights Space Blast." *New York Times*, 7 May 1962, p. 11.

6. Walter Sullivan. "Scientists Ask Delay in H-Shot." *New York Times*, 7 May 1962, p. 9.

7. "Lovell Assails Test." *New York Times*, 30 May 1962, p. 5.

8. "Transcript of the President's News Conference on Foreign and Domestic Problems." *New York Times*, 10 May 1962.

9. Thomas J. Hamilton. "Thant Assails U.S. on A-Blasts in Air." *New York Times*, 6 June 1962, p. 1.

CHAPTER 9

1. Quoted in James Roberts. *The Decisions of Robert S. McNamara* (Miami, 1970), p. 70.

2. Reported in Draft Memorandum, James Webb, NASA administrator to John F. Kennedy, president, November 13, 1962. App. Space Activities of the U.S. Government. Kennedy Library, POF, Departments and Agencies, NASA, 1962, Box 84.

3. Memorandum, Eugene M. Zuckert, secretary of the Air Force, to the president September 4, 1962. SECRET. Sanitized Copy. Released September 24, 1979. Kennedy Library, POF, Departments and Agencies, Air Force, July-December 1962, Box 94a.

4. Francis Vivian Drake. "We're Running the Wrong Race with Russia." *Readers Digest*. August 1963.

5. Memorandum, James E. Webb, administrator NASA, to John F. Kennedy, president, 8/9/63. CONFIDENTIAL. Declassified September 9, 1974. Kennedy Library, POF, Departments and Agencies, NASA, 1963, Box 84.

6. "U.S. Prepares New Proposals for Space Research with Soviet Union: Exchange of Messages, J. F. Kennedy and N. Khrushchev." *Department of State Bulletin*, 12 March 1962.

7. Ray Garthoff. "Banning the Bomb in Outer Space." *International Security*, Winter 1980/81.

8. "Text of President Kennedy's Address to the United Nations General Assembly." *New York Times*, 24 September 1963, p. 23.

9. "Transcript of the President's News Conference." *New York Times*, 18 July 1963; see also Alton Frye. *The Proposal for a Joint Lunar Expedition: Background and Prospects*. Rand Corporation Paper P-2808, January 1964.

10. A. P. Alibrando. "Kennedy's Offer Stirs Confusion, Dismay." *Aviation Week*, 30 September 1963; see also Alibrando. "Kennedy's Plan Stirs Attack on Space Funds." *Aviation Week*, 7 October 1963.

CHAPTER 10

1. Reported in U.S. Congress. *National Space Goals for the Post-Apollo Period*. Hearings before the Committee in Aeronautical and Space Sciences, U.S. Senate, 89th Congress, August 23–25, 1965.

2. U.S. Congress. *National Goals for the Post-Apollo Period*, p. 307–9.

3. Author's interview with General Bernard A. Schriever, USAF Retired, Washington. D.C. January 8, 1983.

4. *Orlando Evening Star,* 4 August 1965. Quoted in NASA Historical Staff. *Astronautics and Aeronautics, 1965,* p. 367.

5. Phyllis Schlafly and Chester Ward. *Strike from Space,* (Alton, Ill., 1965), p. 189.

6. *Air Force Magazine,* October 1965. Quoted in NASA Historical Staff. *Astronautics and Aeronautics, 1965,* p. 499.

7. "Satellites Used to Guide Bombing of North Vietnam." *New York Times,* 14 April 1967, p. 5.

8. *The Space Program in the Post-Apollo Period.* Report of the President's Science Advisory Committee. Prepared by Joint Space Panels, February 1967.

CHAPTER 11

1. *The Post-Apollo Space Program: Directions for the Future.* Space Task Group Report to the President. September 1969.

2. Kurt Vonnegut. "Excelsior! We're Going to the Moon." *New York Times Magazine,* 21 December 1969.

3. Norman Mailer. *Of a Fire on the Moon* (New York, 1971).

4. Quoted in "Shuttle Gives a Lift to Aerospace." *Business Week,* 15 January 1972.

5. Quoted in Michael Klare. *War Without End: American Planning for the Next Vietnams* (New York, 1972), p. 208.

6. Richard DeLauer. "The Force Multiplier." *IEEE Spectrum,* October 1982, p. 36.

CHAPTER 12

1. See Klare. *War Without End,* p. 322.

2. Thomas Winter. "The Army's Role in Space." *Military Review,* July 1968.

3. U.S. Congress. *National Goals for the Post-Apollo Period,* p. 307–8; see also "Brown Views Space for Military Support." *Aviation Week,* 22 April 1963.

CHAPTER 13

1. "Meeting in Space." *New York Times,* 15 July 1975, p. 32.

2. U.S. Congress. *Future Space Programs.* Hearings before the Committee on Science and Technology, U.S. House of Representatives, January 24–26, 1978.

CHAPTER 15

1. "NASA Plans Under Fire." *Los Angeles Times*, 11 April 1973; see also W. J. Normyle. "NASA Divided Over Space Shuttle." *Aviation Week*, 11 May 1970.
2. Bernard Schriever. "Speech before the Aviation Writer's Association. Las Vegas, Nevada, May 15, 1967, in *Vital Speeches of the Day*, 4 December 1967.
3. Air Force Report. Unattributed. CONFIDENTIAL. Sanitized Copy. Released April 7, 1977. Johnson Library, VP Security File, Aircraft, Dyna-Soar Project Streamline Summary.
4. "Summary of Projects Comprising National Space Program." NASA/ Department of Defense Staff Report. June 3, 1961. SECRET. Sanitized copy. Released July 22, 1977. Johnson Library, VP Security File, National Space Program.
5. See U.S. Congress. *Space Transportation System*. Hearings before the Subcommittee on Space Sciences and Applications of the Committee in Science and Technology, U.S. House of Representatives, May 17–18, 1977, p. 108.
6. Quoted in Trudi Bell. "America's Other Space Program." *Spaceworld*, March 1980.
7. Bell. "America's Other Space Program."
8. U.S. Congress. *National Space Policy*. Hearings before the Subcommittee on Space Sciences and Applications of the Committee on Science and Technology, U.S. House of Representatives, May 17–18, 1982.
9. Bell. "America's Other Space Program."

CHAPTER 16

1. This and other quotations that follow are from author's interview with Bernard Schriever on January 8, 1983.
2. Richard Halloran. "Pentagon Draws Up First Strategy for Fighting a Long Nuclear War." *New York Times*, 30 May 1982, p. 1.
3. "Joint Statement, Hon. Verne Orr, Secretary of the Air Force and General Lew Allen, Chief of Staff, U.S. Air Force." In U.S. Congress, *DoD Authorization for Appropriations for FY 1983*. Hearings before the Committee on Armed Services, U.S. Senate, Part 2, p. 946.
4. "U.S. Military Posture: Statement of Secretary of Defense Caspar Weinberger and General John W. Vessey, Jr., Chairman, Joint Chiefs of Staff." In U.S. Congress, *DoD Authorization for Appropriations for FY 1984*. Hearings before the Committee on Armed Services, U.S. Senate, Part 1, p. 172.
5. "Military Official Stresses Need for Survivable Space Systems." *Aviation Week*, 18 May 1981.

6. "U.S. Military Posture." In U.S. Congress, *DoD Authorization for Appropriations for FY 1984*, p. 351.

7. Halloran. "Pentagon Draws Up First Strategy for Fighting a Long Nuclear War."

8. Ibid.

9. U.S. Congress. *Arms Control and the Militarization of Space*. Hearing before the Subcommittee on Arms Control, Oceans, International Operations and Environment of the Committee on Foreign Relations, U.S. Senate, September 20, 1982, p. 31.

10. "Soviets Propose U.N. Treaty to Ban Space Weapons." *Space for All People*, December 1981.

11. Lt. Gen. Daniel O. Graham (Ret.). *High Frontier: A New National Strategy* (Washington, 1982).

12. U.S. Congress. *Arms Control and the Militarization of Space*, p. 37.

13. "Missile Defense Effort Includes Directed Energy, Other Means." *Aviation Week*, 30 May 1983.

14. Quoted in James Canan. *War in Space* (New York, 1982), p. 162.

15. Harold Brown. *Thinking About National Security and Foreign Policy in a Dangerous World* (Boulder, 1983).

16. "President's Speech on Military Spending and a New Defense." Text of Reagan's Speech, March 24, 1983. *New York Times*, 24 March 1983.

CHAPTER 17

1. The material for this chapter is largely drawn from author's interviews with Robert Bowman and Carol Sue Rosin in January 1983.

2. Robert Bowman and Carol Rosin. "The Socio-Economic Benefits of a Global Space Applications Program." International Astronautical Association Paper 81-224. Rome, Italy. September 1981.

3. As noted in Robert Bowman and Maggie Bowman. "Final Report on UNISPACE 82." Unpublished paper prepared for the Friends World Committee.

CHAPTER 18

1. Robert Bowman. "Why All the Fuss Over Weapons in Space." Shadow Cabinet Background Paper #1, October 1982. Shadow Cabinet Foundation.

2. Statement of Daniel Deudney, senior researcher, Worldwatch Institute, On SR 43, SJR 28, and U.S. Military Policy before the Senate Committee on Foreign Relations Subcommittee on Arms Control, Oceans, International Operations and Environment. April 14, 1983. Worldwatch Institute.

Bibliography and Suggestions for Further Reading*

JOURNALS

The most important and influential journal is *Aviation Week and Space Technology* published weekly by McGraw-Hill Publications. *AW&ST* has a strong promilitary bias. It is notorious for publishing selected "leaks" in time to influence key authorization votes in Congress. Still, when read with a critical eye it is an invaluable source of information. The American Institute of Aeronautics and Astronautics (1633 Broadway, New York, NY 10019) puts out the monthly *Aeronautics and Astronautics*. More staid and balanced than *AW&ST*, it supplements the latter's newsworthiness with depth of material and occasionally some analysis. The Institute of Electrical and Electronics Engineers (345 E. 47th St., New York, NY 10017) publishes the *IEEE Spectrum* and occasionally produces special issues that are pertinent to space and war. Two recent examples are "Technology in War and Peace," October 1982, and "Space 25," an overview of topics in space technology and policy, September 1983. An interesting attempt to combine progressive politics with space populism can be found in the quarterly *Space for All People*, published by the Progressive Space Forum (1476 California #9, San Francisco, CA 94109). It is also the only journal in which one can regularly find excellent investigative reporting on military activities in space. *Space World*, published monthly by Palmer Publications (Amherst, WI 54406), in cooperation with the National Space Institute, features clear and simple reporting on difficult issues of policy and technology for a lay readership of space enthusiasts.

Important articles on science in general and space in particular can be found in *Science*, the weekly journal of the American Association for the Advancement of Science (1515 Massachusetts Ave. N.W., Washington D.C. 20005). *The Bulletin of Atomic Scientists* (5801 S. Kenwood, Chicago, IL 60637) is an authoritative voice of scientific conscience covering a wide range of science and technology policy issues. A radical political perspective on science is offered bimonthly in *Science for the People* (897 Main St., Cambridge, MA 02139).

---

* Publishers provided only for books in print.

218

Pop science, British-style, is the theme of *New Scientist* (Commonwealth House, 1-19 New Oxford St., London WC 1A ENG). An occasional gem of space information can be found hidden among its weekly clutter of newsprint. Articles giving an intellectual veneer to Air Force strategy can be found in *Air University Review: The Professional Journal of the United States Air Force*, available from the Government Printing Office.

GENERAL WORKS ON U.S. SPACE ACTIVITIES

An excellent brief overview of space technology and politics, both military and civilian, is provided in Daniel Deudney, *Space: The High Frontier in Perspective* (Washington, D.C.: Worldwatch Institute, 1982). Richard Hutton, *The Cosmic Chase* (New York: New American Library, 1981), is a popularly written and informative space history. General works on the early Space Age and the formation of NASA are Erland A. Kennan and Edmund H. Harvey, *Mission to the Moon: A Critical Examination of NASA and the Space Program* (New York, 1969); Edwin Diamond, *The Rise and Fall of the Space Age* (Garden City, N.Y., 1964); Walter McDougall, "Technocracy and Statecraft in the Space Age—Toward the History of a Saltation," *American Historical Review*, October 1982; John Logsdon, *The Decision to Go to the Moon: Project Apollo and the National Interest* (Chicago: University of Chicago Press, 1970); Emitai Etzioni, *The Moon-Doggle, Domestic and International Implications of the Space Race* (Garden City, N.Y., 1964); R. Jastrow and H. Newell, "The Space Program and the National Interest," *Foreign Affairs*, Fall 1972; Joseph Goldsen (ed.), *Outer Space in World Politics* (New York, 1963). A good attempt to place the discussion of space issues in their economic context is Mary Holman, *The Political Economy of the Space Program* (Palo Alto, CA, 1974). On international and national space law the Senate Committee on Commerce, Science and Transportation's three-volume set *Space Law: Selected Basic Documents* (Washington, D.C.: Government Printing Office, 1978) is indispensable. A point of view from outside the superpower context is provided in S. Bhatt, *Legal Controls of Outer Space* (New Delhi, 1973). An excellent account of some of the stickier issues of space policy is given in George Robinson, "Space Law, Space War and Space Exploitation," *Journal of Social and Political Studies*, Fall 1980. The Congressional Office of Technology Assessment, *Civilian Space Policy and Applications 1982* (Washington, D.C.: Government Printing Office, 1982) gives a general overview of the current civilian space program. On the level of myth and symbol, there is no more biting description of the lust for power implied in rocketry and space travel than in Lewis Mumford, *The Pentagon of Power, Volume II: The Myth of the Machine* (New York, 1970). An exploration of the meaning of the Space Age in view of the moon landing and pictures of earth sent from space can be found in Joseph Campbell, *Myths to Live By* (New York: Viking Press, 1972) and in William Irwin Thompson, *Passages About the Earth* (New York: Harper and Row, 1973). An occasionally stunning and sometimes depressing view of NASA and Apollo is given in Norman Nailer, *Of a Fire on the Moon* (New York: New American Library, 1971). An excellent recreation of the quasireligious sentiment underlying the romantic appeal of space travel is in Oriana Fallaci, *If the Sun Should Fall* (New York, 1965). The same religiosity endows NASA astronauts with knighthood and sainthood in Tom Wolfe, *The Right Stuff* (New York: Farrar, Straus and Giroux, 1981).

GENERAL WORKS OF MILITARY AND POLITICAL ANALYSIS

On U.S. nuclear weapons policies, the background of the intellectual strategic debate is provided in Fred Kaplan, *The Wizards of Armageddon* (New York: Simon and Schuster, 1983). The historical background is given in Sidney Lens, *The Day before Doomsday: An Anatomy of the Nuclear Arms Race* (Boston: Beacon Press, 1977); Michael Armacost, *The Politics of Weapons Innovations* (New York, 1969); Robert Jungke, *Brighter than a Thousand Suns* (London, 1958); Victor Basuch, *Technology, World Politics and American Policy* (New York: Columbia University Press, 1977); Robert Gilpin, *American Scientists and Nuclear Weapons Policy* (New York, 1962). A graphic and painful description of nuclear effects is given in Bulletin of Atomic Scientist (eds.), *The Final Epidemic: Physicians and Scientists on Nuclear War* (Chicago: University of Chicago Press, 1982) and Helen Caldicott, *Nuclear Madness: What You Can Do* (Brookline, MA: Autumn Press, 1978). William Broad, "A Fatal Flaw in the Concept of Space War," *Science*, March 12, 1982, discusses the effects of nuclear explosions in space as does "Satellite Hardening," *Aviation Week and Space Technology*, March 15, 1982, and Wilmot Hess, *The Effects of High Altitude Explosions* (Goddard Space Flight Center: NASA, 1964). Shifts in U.S. nuclear policy are detailed in two pamphlets: Robert Aldrich, *The Counterforce Syndrome: A Guide to U.S. Strategic Doctrine* (Washington, D.C.: Institute for Policy Studies, 1979) and Jerry Elmer, *Limited Nuclear War: America's Counterforce Strategy* (Philadelphia: American Friends Service Committee, 1982). A host of nuclear weapons issues are covered in E. P. Thompson and Dan Smith (eds.), *Protest and Survive* (New York: Monthly Review Press, 1981). Jonathan Schell, *The Fate of the Earth* (New York: Knopf, 1982) gives a devastating look into the meaning of nuclear armageddon. On the matter of science's involvement in the arms race, Joseph Rotblat (ed.), *Scientists, the Arms Race and Disarmament* (London and Paris: UNESCO, 1982) and Adriano Buzzatti-Traverso, *The Scientific Enterprise Today and Tomorrow*

(Paris: UNESCO, 1977) provide valuable insights. Individual stories of a scientist's participation in the arms race are given in Herbert York, *Race to Oblivion: A Participants View of the Arms Race* (New York, 1970); James Killian, *Sputnik, Scientists and Eisenhower: A Memoir of the First Special Assistant to the President for Science and Technology* (Cambridge, MA: M.I.T. Press, 1977); and "The Arms Race and Nuclear War: An Interview with George Kistiakowsky," *Chemical and Engineering News*, February 2, 1981, and reprinted in Thompson and Smith, *Protest and Survive*. A brief general discussion of the nuclear arms race can be found in Phillip Morrison, "The Spiral of Peril: A Narrative of the Nuclear Arms Race," *Bulletin of Atomic Scientists*, January 1983. Norman Moss, *Men Who Play God* (New York, 1968) gives a critical account of the same. Debates surrounding the test ban negotiations are contained in Robert Divine, *Blowing on the Wind: The Nuclear Test Ban Debate* (New York: Oxford University Press, 1978). A general discussion of ABM systems and foreign and military policies is in C. F. Barnaby and A. Boserup (eds.), *Implications of AntiBallistic Missile Systems*, Pugwash Monograph II (New York: The Humanities Press, 1969). For an insight into early limited nuclear war strategizing, see Henry Kissinger, *Nuclear Weapons and Foreign Policy* (New York, 1957). Nuclear doctrine in the age of Reagan is described in Richard Halloran, "Pentagon Draws Up First Strategy for Fighting a Long Nuclear War," *New York Times*, May 30, 1982. The intellectual justification for such a strategy can be found in Colin Gray, "Victory is Possible," *Foreign Affairs*, Summer 1980. Both Soviet and American nuclear strategies are considered in Eric J. Lerner, "Major Power Strategies," *IEEE Spectrum*, October 1982. Harold Brown, *Thinking About National Security: Defense and Foreign Policy in a Dangerous World* (Boulder, CO: Worldview Press, 1983) presents a Democratic alternative to Reagan's defense strategies. For a progressive internationalist alternative to the nuclear arms race, see Johan Galtung, *The True Worlds: A Transnational Perspective* (New York: Free Press, 1981). Pam McAllister (ed.), *Reweaving the Web of Life: Feminism and Nonviolence* (Philadelphia: Movement for a New Society, 1982) brings a refreshing feminist perspective to the issues of foreign and military policy and nuclear weapons.

General works on the Cold War often give conflicting analyses. The case made in this book concerning the roots of the Cold War and its long-term effects on military space developments is based largely on William Appleman Williams, *The Tragedy of American Diplomacy* (Garden City, NY, 1961); Walter LaFeber, *America, Russia and the Cold War, 1945-1966* (New York, 1967); Nathan and Oliver, *United States Foreign Policy and World Order* (Boston: Little-Brown, 1976); Thomas Larson, *Soviet-American Rivalry* (New York: Norton, 1978); Alan Wolfe, *The Rise and Fall of the "Soviet Threat": Domestic Sources of the Cold War Consensus* (Washington, D.C.: Institute for Policy Studies, 1980); David Halloway, *The Soviet Union and the Arms Race* (New

Haven: Yale University Press, 1983); Joseph Nogee and Robert Donaldson, *Soviet Foreign Policy since World War II* (New York: Pergamon Press, 1981). The significance and results of NSC 68 are discussed in John Lewis Gaddis, "NSC 68 and the Problem of Ends and Means," and Samuel F. Wells, Jr., "Sounding the Tocsin: NSC 68 and the Soviet Threat," both in *International Security*, Spring 1980. See also Kaplan, *The Wizards of Armageddon*. The report itself is "NSC-68: A Report to the President Pursuant to the Presidential Directive of January 31, 1950 from Secretaries of State and Defense, April 7, 1950." For the perspective from the White House, see Dwight D. Eisenhower, *Waging Peace 1956-1961*, Volume II, *The White House Years* (New York: Doubleday, 1963). Blanche Wiessen-Cook, *The DeClassified Eisenhower* (New York: Doubleday, 1981) provides background information on the Eisenhower presidency. Further background information on individual members of the Eisenhower administration can be found in Philip Burch, *Elites in American History: The New Deal to the Carter Administration*, Volume III, *Elites in American History* (New York: Holmes and Meier, 1980). Contemporary reporting on the disappearance of the "missile gap" appear in "Missile Gap Widens Against Russia," *US News & World Report*, November 19, 1962; "Whatever Happened to the Missile Gap," *US News & World Report*, April 16, 1962; and "McNamara Says U.S. Is Capable of Destroying All Soviet Targets; Summary of Report," *Aviation Week and Space Technology*, January 19, 1962.

The best analysis of global power in the post–Cold War period can be found in Richard Barnet, *The Lean Years: Politics in the Age of Scarcity* (New York: Simon and Schuster, 1980). America's global military strategy in the post-Vietnam era is analyzed in Michael Klare, *War Without End: American Planning for the Next Vietnams* (New York, 1972); Michael Klare, *Beyond the Vietnam Syndrome: U.S. Interventionism in the 1980s* (Washington, D.C.: Institute for Policy Studies, 1980); and Michael Klare, "Resurgent Militarism," Issue Paper of the Institute for Policy Studies, 1981. The reemergence of Cold War ideology, even before the Reagan presidency, is detailed in Noam Chomsky, *Towards a New Cold War* (New York: Pantheon, 1982).

ORIGINS OF ROCKETRY AND SPACE FLIGHT

The basics are well covered in Wernher von Braun and Frederick Ordway, *History of Rocketry and Space Travel* (New York, 1966). The efforts of Von Braun's World War II rocket team are recounted in F. Ordway and M. Sharpe, *The Rocket Team* (New York: Crowell, 1979). Biographies of Von Braun are James L. Daniels, "A Biography of Wernher von Braun" in Ernst Stuhlinger (ed.), *Astronautical Engineering and Science, from Peenemunde to Planetary Science* (Washington, D.C., 1962); and Erik Bergaust, *Wernher von Braun*

(Washington, D.C., 1976). Early speculations on the future of space flight are in Cornelius Ryan (ed.), *Across the Space Frontier* (New York, 1952). Initial speculations on the potential uses of orbiting satellites by American military scientists can be found in "Preliminary Design of an Experimental World-Circling Spaceship," RAND Study Memorandum–11827. The work of Hermann Oberth, including his proposed space mirror, is detailed in Frank Winter, "Space Stations: Circa 1920s," *Vectors*, Fall 1982. Also see "German Space Mirror," *Life*, July 23, 1945. On the Dyna-Soar's origins in German space research see Walter Dornberger, "Military Utilization of Space," *Aviation Week and Space Technology*, September 18, 1961; and "Dyna-Soar's History Full of Reexaminations," *Aviation Week and Space Technology*, August 22, 1963.

On the Soviet roots, see Nikolai D. Anoschenko, (ed.), *A History of Aviation and Cosmonautics* (Washington, 1977) and F. J. Krieger, *Soviet Astronautics*, RAND Corporation Paper, P-1437, February 24, 1958.

MILITARY PLANS FOR SPACE 1955–1968

For the political atmosphere created in the United States by Sputnik, see W. C. Davidon, "Soviet Satellites; US Reactions," *Bulletin of Atomic Scientists*, December 1957; "No Reason to Grow Hysterical. News Conference of Dwight D. Eisenhower, 10/9/57," *US News & World Report*, October 18, 1957; Dwight D. Eisenhower, "Summary of Important Facts in Earth Satellite Program," *U.S. Department of State Bulletin*, October 28, 1957. An interesting summary of the state of space and missile projects in the late 1950s is in Donald Cox and Michael Stoiko, *Spacepower: What It Means to You* (Philadelphia, 1958). Air Force Magazine (ed.), *Space Weapons: A Handbook of Military Astronautics* (London, 1959) includes a history of the X series of Air Force research planes and a description of early space weapons proposals. Much information can be gleaned from congressional hearings of the time. Most important are U.S. Congress, *Missiles, Space and Other Major Defense Matters*, Hearings before the Preparedness Investigating Subcommittee of the Committee on Armed Services in conjunction with the Committee on Aeronautical and Space Sciences, U.S. Senate, February 2, 3, 4, 8, 9 and March 16, 1960; *Missile Development and Space Sciences*, Hearings before the Committee on Science and Astronautics, U.S. House of Representatives, February and March 1959; *Investigation of Governmental Organization for Space Activities*, Hearings before the Subcommittee on Government Operations for Space Activities of the Committee on Aeronautical and Space Sciences, U.S. Senate, March and April 1959; *Missile and Space Activities*, Joint Hearings before the Preparedness Investigating Subcommittee of the Committee on Armed Services and the Committee on Aeronautical and Space Sciences, U.S. Senate, January 29–30, 1959. Both generals and civilian scientists presented their visions of the future to the staff that prepared *The Next Ten Years in Space*, Staff Report of the Select Committee on Astronautics and Space Exploration, U.S. House of Representatives, June 1959. For reports on the Air Force's plans to establish a missile base on the moon, see "Military May Accelerate Lunar Base Plan," *Aviation Week*, September 29, 1958; "USAF Considering Moon Base by 1968," *Aviation Week*, April 27, 1959; and "Military Use Seen for Base on the Moon," *Aviation Week*, October 26, 1959, in addition to the congressional hearings cited. On military plans for manned space vehicles, see "Program Aimed at Manned Space Flight Started by USAF Group," *Aviation Week*, December 3, 1956; J. S. Butz, "Hypersonic Glider Studied as Manned Missile Hope," *Aviation Week*, March 18, 1957. The first space ABM proposals are detailed in "ARPA Studies Satellite-Borne Anti-ICBM Defense System," *Aviation Week*, October 31, 1960; Phillip Klass, "BAMBI ICBM Defense Concept Analyzed," *Aviation Week*, October 23, 1961. BAMBI and the moon-base concepts are outlined in "Fantastic Weaponry," in Fortune Magazine (ed.), *The Space Industry: America's Newest Giant* (New York, 1962). Details of the debate over how the U.S. space program should be organized and who should control it are to be found in the congressional hearings cited as well as "Congress Draws Battle Lines for Outer-Space Control," *Aviation Week*, February 3, 1958; "Space Warfare: Should Control of Outer Space Be Civilian or Military?" *Newsweek*, February 10, 1958; "Transfer of Projects Gives Air Force Major Role in Military Space Activities," *Science*, October 9, 1959.

The efforts of Bernard Schriever and the Air Force study committee on space to influence the new administration of John Kennedy toward giving the military preeminence in the nation's space program can be seen in "Military Space Technology Needs Are Urgent," *Aviation Week and Space Technology*, September 25, 1961; Trevor Gardner, "High Priority Military Space Race Urged," *Aviation Week and Space Technology*, October 9, 1961; "Arms in Space: Something Else to Worry About," *US News & World Report*, October 9, 1961; "Air Force Bids for Key Role in Space," *Business Week*, October 21, 1961; G. Alexander, "USAF Aims at Military Space Supremacy," *Aviation Week and Space Technology*, October 2, 1961. As part of a public relations campaign, there appeared a profile of Bernard Schriever by D. Schlanche, "General of Outer Space," *Saturday Evening Post*, October 7, 1961.

On the Defense Department side of the Air Force-DoD debate, see "DoD Balks at Most Military Space Expansions Except in Reconnaissance," *Aviation Week and Space Technology*, March 11, 1963; "Brown Views Space for Military Support," *Aviation Week and Space Technology*, April 22, 1963. James Roberts, *Decisions of Robert McNamara* (Miami, 1970) explores the many difficult choices faced by the Defense Secretary. For an example of a conservative attack on McNamara for shortchanging the military in space see Hanson Baldwin, "Slow Down in the Pentagon," *Foreign Affairs*, January 1965.

Information on Project MOL and the military involvement in Project Gemini can be found in many of the general works cited and in Eldon Downs (ed.), *The U.S. Air Force in Space* (New York, 1966); and in the following articles: L. Carter, "Space: MOL to Give Military First Chance at Manned Flight," *Science*, September 17, 1965; "MOL Increases Opportunities in Military Space Activities," *Aviation Week and Space Technology*, March 6, 1967; "Air Force Given Manned Space Role: MOL Program," *Aviation Week and Space Technology*, August 30, 1965; "For $1.5 Billion, a New Air Force Eye in the Sky: MOL," *Newsweek*, September 6, 1965; "Next: Military Mastery of Space? Potential of Project Gemini," *US News & World Report*, June 14, 1965; W. H. Gregory, "DoD, NASA Agree on Gemini Experiments," *Aviation Week and Space Technology*, June 1, 1964.

President Kennedy's offer to the Soviets to join with the United States in a cooperative lunar program is explored in Alton Frye, *The Proposal for a Joint Lunar Expedition: Background and Prospects*, RAND Corporation Paper P-2808, January 1964; A. P. Alibrando, "Kennedy's Offer Stirs Confusion, Dismay," *Aviation Week and Space Technology*, September 30, 1963. For the background of the debate over Soviet-American cooperation in space see D. S. Greenberg, "Space Accord: NASA's Enthusiasm for East-West Cooperation Is Not Shared by Pentagon," *Science*, April 13, 1962.

On U.S. nuclear weapons tests in space, see U.S. Congress, *Project Argus*, a Report from the Committee on Science and Astronautics, U.S. House of Representatives, July 29, 1959; "Triumph in Space for a Crazy Greek," *Life*, March 30, 1959; "White House Reports on Scientific Aspects of Radiation Belts Created by Argus Experiments," April 10, 1959; "Argus Potential as Weapon Described; Testimony before Senate Subcommittee on Governmental Organization for Space Activities," *Aviation Week*, April 6, 1959; Declassified Documents Reference System 77, 355D, *Report on Argus*, Memorandum: J. R. Killian, Special Assistant to the President for Science and Technology, to the President, November 3, 1958; E. Clark, "Argus Radiation Hit 4,000 Mile Altitude," *Aviation Week*, March 30, 1959; Ney and Kellogg, "Geophysical Effects Associated with High Altitude Explosions," *Nature*, February 7, 1959; Wilmot Hess, *The Effects of High Altitude Explosions* (Goddard Space Flight Center: NASA, 1964); Declassified Documents Reference System 78, 1B, AEC *Proposed Tests*, Memorandum: Glenn T. Seaborg, Chairman, AEC, to the National Council, February 16, 1962; "Now the Rainbow Bomb," *The Nation*, May 12, 1962; "Military Scientists Proposed US Megaton Shots in and above the Ionosphere," *The Nation*, May 19, 1962; Lord Ritchie Calder, "Mortgaging the Old Homestead," *Foreign Affairs*, Spring 1970.

POST-APOLLO TO THE SHUTTLE

A valuable source for reconstructing the early debates over the post-Apollo space program is U.S. Congress, *National Goals for the Post-Apollo Period*, Hearings before the Committee on Aeronautical and Space Sciences, U.S. Senate, August 23-25, 1965. See also U.S. Congress, *Future National Space Objectives*, Hearings before the Subcommittee on NASA Oversight of the Committee on Science and Astronautics, U.S. House of Representatives, July 1966; U.S. Congress, *Future NASA Space Programs*, Hearings before the Committee on Aeronautical and Space Sciences, U.S. Senate, August 5, 1969; Joint Space Panels, *The Space Program in the Post-Apollo Period*, President's Science Advisory Committee Report, February 1967; "To Mars, Slowly: Recommendations of the Space Task Group," *Newsweek*, September 29, 1969; "Can the U.S. Merge the Two Space Rivals? NASA and the Air Force," *Business Week*, September 14, 1968; "Nixon Backs Space Future," *Aviation Week and Space Technology*, December 1, 1969; "Post-Apollo Focuses on Orbital Programs," *Aviation Week and Space Technology*, July 14, 1969; "After Apollo, What?" *Scientific American*, April 1967. For background material on the space shuttle program Jarry Grey, *Enterprise* (New York: Morrow, 1979) is the most insightful and entertaining. Marshall Kaplan, *Space Shuttle: America's Wings into the Future* (Fallbrook, CA, 1978) gives an engineer's inside view of the shuttle development and some of its problems. Howard Alloway, *The Space Shuttle at Work* (Washington: NASA, 1979) is a government public relations job. See also U.S. Congress, *Space Transportation System*, Hearings before the Subcommittee on Space Science and Applications of the Committee on Science and Technology, U.S. House of Representatives, May 17-18, 1977. For what I have called Schriever's "dilemma," see Bernard Schriever, "Speech before the Aviation and Space Writer's Association, Las Vegas, NV, May 15, 1967," *Vital Speeches of the Day*, December 4, 1967. The economic motive behind the space shuttle approval can be understood by seeing U.S. Congress, *State of the Aerospace Industry*, Hearing before the Committee on Aeronautical and Space Sciences, U.S. Senate, September 26-27, 1973. See also "Shuttle Gives a Lift to Aerospace," *Business Week*, January 15, 1972. Further sources of information on the space shuttle's beginnings are U.S. Congress, *Space Shuttle—Skylab: Manned Space Flight in the 1970s*, Status Report for the Committee on NASA Oversight of the Committee on Science and Technology, U.S. House of Representatives, June 1970; "Reusable Space Shuttle Efforts Gain Momentum," *Aviation Week and Space Technology*, October 27, 1969; "Shuttle Dominates Post-Apollo Era," *Aviation Week and Space Technology*, December 14, 1969; "USAF Studies Shuttle Missions," *Aviation Week and Space Technology*, November 8, 1971; R. Gilette, "Space Shuttle: A Giant Step for NASA and the Military," *Science*, March 12, 1971; "Joint Space Shuttle

Program Mapped by NASA and the Air Force," *Aviation Week and Space Technology*, May 7, 1973; "Military to Drop Present Boosters for NASA Space Shuttle System," *Aviation Week and Space Technology*, April 5, 1971; "Space Shuttle: National Defense," *Space World*, September 1973.

On the Apollo-Soyuz mission Ezell and Ezell, *The Partnership: A History of the Apollo-Soyuz Test Project* (Washington: NASA, 1978) presents a complete account but lacks a critical viewpoint. On the early planning for Apollo-Soyuz and some of the questions raised by it, see U.S. Congress, *Manned Spaceflight: U.S.-Soviet Rendezvous and Docking*. Hearing before the Subcommittee on Science and Astronautics, U.S. House of Representatives, May 31, 1972. For a typical sample of attacks on Apollo-Soyuz from the Right, see "Who's Detenting Whom? Apollo Soyuz Test Project," *National Review*, November 21, 1975.

On the militarization of the shuttle, see "Bigger Role for Military in Space; Growing Interest in Shuttle," *US News and World Report*, April 26, 1976; "Defense Chief Terms Manned Shuttle Vital to Military Plans," *New York Times*, July 28, 1980; John Noble Wilford, "About a Fourth of NASA Budget for Research Is Said to Be Military," *New York Times*, May 3, 1982; R. Lyons, "Military Planners View Shuttle as Way to Open Space for Warfare," *New York Times*, March 29, 1981; J. R. Smith, "Military Plans for Shuttle Stir Concern," *Science*, May 1, 1981; D. Dooling, "Air Force Has Secret Flight Planned," *Space World*, July 1981; D. Dooling, "USAF Cargo for Space Shuttle," *Space World*, July 1982.

GENERAL WORKS ON THE MILITARIZATION OF SPACE

The best account of the current round of space militarization is given in Thomas Karras, *The New High Ground: Strategies and Tactics of Space Age War* (New York: Simon and Schuster, 1983). Also of use are David Ritchie, *Spacewar* (New York: Atheneum, 1982) and James Canan, *War in Space* (New York: Harper and Row, 1982). The Stockholm Peace Research Institute has published two studies: Bhupendra Jasani (ed.), *Outer Space—Battlefield of the Future?* and Jasani (ed.), *Outer Space—A New Dimension of the Arms Race* (Stockholm: Oelgeschlager, Gunn & Hain, 1982). Both works contain informative tables listing and describing most, if not all, Soviet and American military launches.

There is a subgenre of prospacewar works. Michael Golovine, *Conflict in Space: A Pattern of War in a New Dimension* (London, 1962) is the first book to argue that because war in space would involve no civilians it would be a preferable form of warfare. Robert Salkeld, *War and Space* (Garden City, NY, 1970) makes an elaborate case in favor of militarizing deep space instead of near-earth space, the region to be covered by most space weapons systems currently under development. See also Stewart Brand, "War in Space: Good," *New Scientist*, May 28, 1981. Other general sources on space militarization are U.S. Congress, *Arms Control and the Militarization of Space*, Hearing before the Subcommittee on Arms Control, Oceans, International Operations and Environment of the Committee on Foreign Relations. U.S. Senate, September 20, 1982; Stanley Foundation, *Cooperation or Confrontation in Outer Space*, Thirteenth Conference on the United Nations of the Next Decade, Iowa City, July 9-15, 1978 (Muscatine, Iowa: Stanley Foundation, 1978); George C. Wilson, "Reagan's Space Policy Colored USAF Blue," *Astronautics and Aeronautics*, September 1982; Bruce Conklin, "The Arms Race Takes Off: The Pentagon's Takeover of NASA and the Militarization of Space," *Westword*, August 26, 1982; Kosta Tsipsis, "Military Competition in Space," in *Strategy for Peace*, Stanley Foundation Conference on US Foreign Policy, October 16-18, 1981 (Muscatine, Iowa: Stanley Foundation, 1981); Trudi Bell, "America's Other Space Program," *Space World*, March 1980; "The New Military Race in Space," *Business Week*, June 4, 1979; Arthur C. Clarke, "War and Peace in the Space Age," Address to the UN Committee on Disarmament, Geneva, August 31, 1982 in *Congressional Record*, September 21, 1982; John Noble Wilford, "Buildup in Space: A New Military Focus," three-part series, *New York Times*, October 17-19, 1982.

MILITARY SATELLITES AND GLOBAL C^3&I

In addition to the general works cited above, see B. A. Smith, "Emphasis on Military Systems to Grow," *Aviation Week and Space Technology*, March 3, 1980, and B. A. Smith, "Military Satellite Emphasis Increases," *Aviation Week and Space Technology*, January 29, 1979. General information about reconnaissance satellites can be found in Jasani (ed.), *Outer Space* and Karas, *The New High Ground*. For more background, see Philip Klass, *Secret Sentries in Space* (New York: Random House, 1971) and S. Hochman and S. Wong, *Satellite Spies: The Frightening Impact of a New Technology* (Indianapolis, 1976). A good description of Big Bird appears in Trudi Bell, "America's Other Space Program," *Space World*, March 1980. See also Philip Klass, "Big Bird Nears Full Operational Status," *Aviation Week and Space Technology*, September 25, 1972; "Big Bird—America's Spy in Space," *Space World*, January 1978; "KH-11 Recon Satellite, NAVSTAR Launched From Vandenburg," *Aviation Week and Space Technology*, February 18, 1980. For background on NAVSTAR satellites, see Robert Aldrich, "Dead on Target; NAVSTAR's first strike capability," *The Nation*, October 21, 1978; R. P. DeNaro, "NAVSTAR: The All-Purpose Satellite," *IEEE Spectrum* May 1981;

Geoff Richards, "NAVSTAR—A Complete Global Navigation System," *Spaceflight*, January 1980. For an excellent descriptive article on communication satellites, see Mike Chan, "AFSATCOM: US Space-Based Strategic Communications Systems," *Space for all People*, December 1980. See also *Department of Defense Authorization for Appropriations*, Hearings before the Committee on Armed Services, for general descriptions of existing satellite systems and rationales for proposed systems. For general background information, see Thomas Karas, *Implications of Space Technology for Strategic Nuclear Competition*, Stanley Foundation Occasional Paper #25 (Muscatine, Iowa: Stanley Foundation, 1981).

On the emphasis placed on satellite survivability, see, "Pentagon Increases Stress on Satellite Survivability," *Aviation Week and Space Technology*, April 1, 1974; Erik Lerner, "Strategic C^3: A Goal Unreached," *IEEE Spectrum*, October, 1982; William Broad, "A Fatal Flaw in the Concept of Space War," *Science*, March 12, 1982; B. Miller, "USAF Pushes Satellite Survivability," *Aviation Week and Space Technology*, March 28, 1979; Samuel Tennant, "Space Systems: Can They Withstand Attack?" *IEEE Spectrum*, October 1982; "Spacecraft Survivability Boost Sought," *Aviation Week and Space Technology*, June 16, 1980; B. A. Smith, "New Satellite Systems Designed for Survivability," *Aviation Week and Space Technology*, January 18, 1982; Philip Klass, "U.S. Seeking Better Command Control Survivability," *Aviation Week and Space Technology*, June 23, 1980; W. B. Scott, "Radiation Hardening Found Effective," *Aviation Week and Space Technology*, March 15, 1982; "Military Official Stresses Need for Survivable Space Systems," *Aviation Week and Space Technology*, May 18, 1981; "Satellite Hardening," *Aviation Week and Space Technology*, March 15, 1982; William Broad, "Nuclear Pulse (II): Ensuring Delivery of the Doomsday Signal," *Science*, June 7, 1981.

Weapons for Space

For the study that accelerated the most recent round of the military race in space, see Lt. General Daniel O. Graham, *High Frontier: A New National Strategy* (Washington: The Heritage Foundation, 1982). For a background to Reagan's Star Wars speech and Teller's space weapon, see, "Star Wars: Teller's Futuristic Vision," reprinted from the *Los Angeles Times* in *Syracuse Post-Standard*, August 9, 1983. For a retired admiral's thoughts, see Eugene Carroll, Jr., "War in Space: The US Has Nothing to Gain," reprinted from the *Los Angeles Herald Examiner*, August 6, 1982 in the *Congressional Record*, September 21, 1982. Barry Smernoff, "The Strategic Value of Space-Based Lasers," *Air University Review*, March-April 1982, presents the strategic logic behind space weapons. Another example of a high-tech strategy is in Perry and

230   *Bibliography*

Roberts, "Winning Through Sophistication: How to Meet the Soviet Threat," *Technology Review*, July 1982. Two good background pieces are Richard Garwin, "Are We on the Verge of an Arms Race in Space?" *Bulletin of Atomic Scientists*, May 1981 and B. Schneider, "Preventing Star Wars," *Bulletin of Atomic Scientists*, October 1981. See also Robert Bowman, "Why All the Fuss Over Weapons in Space?" Background Paper #1, Shadow Cabinet Foundation, October 1982.

For background on antisatellite weapons, see Robert Aldrich, "Who Will Shoot First in Space?" *The Nation*, March 25, 1978; C. Covault, "U.S. Pushes Antisatellite Effort," *Aviation Week and Space Technology*, July 17, 1978; Michel Michaud, "The Anti-Satellite Program a Threat to Space Humanization," in *The Space Humanization Series* (Washington: Institute for the Social Science Study of Space, 1979); Stephen Meyer, "Antisatellite Weapons and Arms Control: Incentives and Disincentives from the Soviet and American Perspectives," *International Journal*, Fall 1981; B. A. Smith, "Vought Tests Small Antisatellite System," *Aviation Week and Space Technology*, November 12, 1981.

On Soviet proposals to ban weapons in space, see "Soviets Propose U.N. Treaty to Ban Space Weapons," *Space for All People*, December 1981, and "Soviets Seek Pacts to Ban Space Arms," *Washington Times*, August 4, 1982.

On laser weapons and space-based ABM systems, see Ron Jones, "Space-based ABM Systems Play a Destabilizing Role," *Space for All People*, August 1980; Jim Heaphy, "Hawks Push Space Lasers," *Space for All People*, August 1980; Jim Heaphy, "Space Laser Plan Tied to MX Missile," *Space for All People*, July 1981; Kosta Tsipsis, "Laser Weapons," *Scientific American*, December 1981; Eve Selene, "Laser Weapons Showdown," *Space for All People*, July 1982; C. A. Robinson, "Defense Department Backs Space-based Missile Defense," *Aviation Week and Space Technology*, September 27, 1982; Kosta Tsipsis, "Laser Weapons Fairy Tales," *Christian Science Monitor*, April 7, 1982; "Missile Defense Includes Directed Energy, Other Means," *Aviation Week and Space Technology*, May 30, 1983; C. Robinson, "Beam Weapons Advances Emerge," *Aviation Week and Space Technology*, July 18, 1983.

Finally, on approaches to the use of space technology for an international peacekeeping effort, see the "U.N. Study on the Implications of Establishing an International Satellite Monitoring Agency," A/AC.206/14, August 6, 1981, and Cadi Kaplan, "International Approaches to Peacekeeping," *IEEE Spectrum*, October 1982. Daniel Deudney, *Whole Earth Security: A Geopolitics of Peace*, Worldwatch Paper #55 (Washington: Worldwatch Institute, 1983) is an excellent overview of the issues involved in global security.

Index

231